THE TROPICAL WORLD

GEOGRAPHIES FOR ADVANCED STUDY.
Edited by Professor S. H. BEAVER, M.A.

THE SOVIET UNION. The Land and its People.
By Professor G. JORRÉ.
Translated by E. D. LABORDE, Ph.D.

THE TROPICAL WORLD. Its Social and Economic
Conditions and Its Future Status.
By Professor P. GOUROU.
Translated by E. D. LABORDE, Ph.D.

MALAYA, INDONESIA, BORNEO AND THE PHILIPPINES.
By Professor C. ROBEQUAIN.
Translated by E. D. LABORDE, Ph.D. (*In the Press.*)

Other volumes in preparation.

THE TROPICAL WORLD

*Its Social and Economic Conditions
and Its Future Status*

by

PIERRE GOUROU

Professor at the Collège de France
and at the Free University of Brussels

TRANSLATED BY

E. D. LABORDE

Sometime Assistant Master in Harrow School

1724

LONGMANS, GREEN AND CO
LONDON • NEW YORK • TORONTO

LONGMANS, GREEN AND CO LTD
6 & 7 CLIFFORD STREET LONDON W 1
ALSO AT MELBOURNE AND CAPE TOWN
LONGMANS, GREEN AND CO INC
55 FIFTH AVENUE NEW YORK 3
LONGMANS, GREEN AND CO
215 VICTORIA STREET TORONTO 1
ORIENT LONGMANS LTD
BOMBAY CALCUTTA MADRAS

First published 1953

The original edition of this work was published by Presses Universitaires de France, Paris; copyright in the English Language in the Berne Convention Countries by Longmans, Green and Co. Ltd.

PRINTED IN GREAT BRITAIN BY
SPOTTISWOODE, BALLANTYNE AND CO. LTD.
LONDON AND COLCHESTER

PREFACE

THE more advanced countries of the world have seen their interest in tropical lands fully awakened. The increasing demand for rubber, coffee, cocoa, and other products of the hot belt, the growth of humanitarian feeling towards the peoples of that belt, and the rise of nationalism among the latter have all attracted attention. Great Britain, who is responsible for a larger part of the hot belt than any other nation, has devoted huge sums to the development of her tropical 'colonies.' It seems proper, therefore, that the conditions existing in the hot belt, and especially those related to disease and soil, should be known to people in this country. What are the prospects of the tropical lands and their peoples? How can the tropics best play its part in the world? These questions are answered by M. Gourou in a book which should be in the hands of every colonial administrator and planter. The author has had first-hand acquaintance with the tropics, having resided in Indo-China for some years and visited different parts of tropical and equatorial Africa and South America. The present translation has been brought up to date by him and owes most of its photographic illustrations to his camera. The translator is grateful to him for reading the typescript and for the many additions he has made to the English version of his text. The only departure from the arrangement of the French edition is the placing of the chapter summaries in the list of contents instead of at the heads of the chapters.

E. D. L.

Cholsey,
    December 12, 1952.

CONTENTS

vii

MAPS

PHOTOGRAPHS

xi

Photographs are by the author unless otherwise
acknowledged.

CHAPTER 1

DENSITY OF POPULATION

HITHERTO lands with a hot, wet climate have proved less favourable than the temperate belt as an environment for man. The problems connected with the use of natural resources are not presented in the same way in the two belts, for hot, wet lands have their own special physical and human geography.

The following pages deal with lands which have a mean monthly temperature of at least 65° F. and get enough rain for agriculture to be possible without irrigation. This definition is not meant to be rigid and may be departed from in special cases; and it includes both the equatorial and tropical climates. For the sake of brevity the term 'tropical' will often be used to denote countries with a hot, wet climate.[1]

Thus defined (see Fig. 1), the hot, wet regions have an area of 14·5 million square miles: 3 million in Asia and the East Indies, 750,000 in Melanesia, Australia, and Oceania, 5·75 million in Africa,

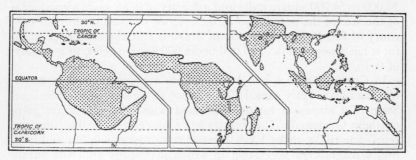

FIG. 1. The belt of hot, wet lands

and 5 million in America. This is a considerable fraction of the earth's dry land and an even more remarkable proportion of its

[1] See below, Fig. 9, p. 60. Many interesting attempts have been made to express the notions of temperature and rainfall in a single numerical index. No description of them can be undertaken here, but the reader is referred to the very useful map merely representing facts and compiled by F. R. Falkner for inclusion with his article 'Die Trockengrense des Regenfeldbaus in Afrika' in *Petermanns G. Mitteilungen*, 1938, pp. 210–14. The map on p. 60 was taken from this work. See also the same author's thesis: *Beiträge zur Agrargeographie der Afrikanischen Trockengebiete*, Basle, 1939, 76 pp.

useful parts. In fact, if the area without value to man is estimated at 17·4 million square miles, the hot, wet belt covers rather more than one-third of the useful portions of the earth's surface.

Most hot, wet lands are sparsely peopled. This fact is surprising at first sight, for these regions support a luxuriant natural vegetation, which seems to betoken conditions favourable to agriculture. But in about 1938 the hot, wet parts of America had a mean density of 2 persons to the square mile; those in Africa between 2 and 3; New Guinea between 0·5 and 0·75; whilst those in Australia were, at any rate outside Queensland, almost uninhabited.

The vast Amazon region[1] is practically empty (see Fig. 2). The Brazilian State of Amazonas has a population of 438,000 to 710,000 square miles (a density of 0·61), that of Matto Grosso one of 354,000 to 500,000 square miles (a density of 0·72), the Amazonian territories of Venezuela, Colombia, Ecuador, and Peru are scarcely better off, and the Peruvian Province of Madre de Dios in the Amazon valley had a density of 0·06 in the census of 1940. The basins of the Orinoco and Amazon are uninhabited wastes of dense vegetation.[2] British Guiana contains 5 persons to the square mile, Dutch Guiana 4, and French Guiana 0·8, whilst the Brazilian territory of Amapá, which is adjacent to French Guiana and has a population of 30,000 to 54,000 square miles and a density of 0·56, gives a good idea of the size of the population in the interior of Guiana. But the territory of Rio Branco del Norte in Brazil is still less densely peopled for it has a population of 15,000 on 96,000 square miles, or a density of 0·16.

In Central America and Mexico there are uninhabited expanses like the region aptly named *El Desierto*[3] in the east of the Mexican State of Chiapas, a region continued with similar features into northern Guatemala. The country has a moderately broken surface-relief, fine rivers, many lakes, mineral resources of sulphur and iron ore, a magnificent vegetation in which mahogany and wild cacao flourish, and a plentiful fauna including many species, like turkeys, pheasants, tapirs, wild boars, deer, antelopes, agutis, and edible fish from Lake Miramar. Yet it is almost uninhabited.

Tropical Africa has a population of 104 million on its 5,790,000 square miles of surface, *i.e.* 18 persons to the square mile. As a whole the centre of the continent seems to be the most thinly peopled part

---

[1] The author has recently set out the data of the problem of population density in the Amazon region in an article entitled 'L'Amazonie: problèmes géographiques' in *Les Cahiers d'Outre-Mer*, Bordeaux, 1949, pp. 1–13.
[2] They are well described by Mr. Earl Hanson in *Geog. Review*, 1933, p. 578.
[3] *Geog. Review*, 1937, p. 28.

with 19 million persons to its 2,624,800 square miles or 7·2 per square mile. Belgian Congo has a density of 12, Angola 1·0, French Equatorial Africa outside the Sahara 0·65, and the French trust area of the Cameroons 26. East Africa, with an area of 1,061,500 square

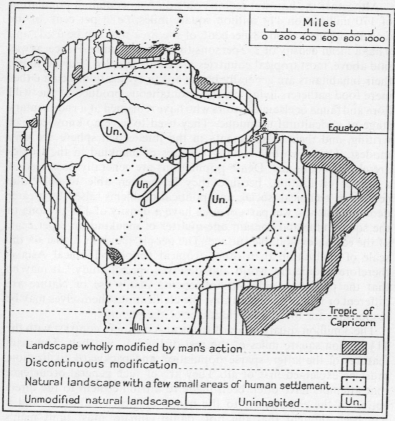

FIG. 2. Man's influence on nature in South America

(After F. Jaeger, 'Versuch einer Anthropogeographischen Gliederung der Erdoberfläche,' in *Petermanns G. Mitteilungen*, 1934)

miles, has a population of 22 million and owes its relative density (3·1) to a few small thickly peopled areas,[1] for outside these the population is no denser than in the central region. West Africa is better off, having a population of 43 million on 1,273,000 square miles and a density of 34. Yet vast expanses are very thinly peopled.[2] Thus, the

[1] See below, pp. 85–93.   [2] See below, pp. 93–9.

density of the hot, wet parts of Anglo-Egyptian Sudan hardly exceeds 2·3. In the tropical parts of South Africa densities are generally low; Southern Rhodesia, for instance, has 14 persons to the square mile, and Madagascar 18.

Altogether the hot, wet regions outside Asia contain a population of 170 millions on 11½ million square miles, *i.e.* 8 per cent. of the world's population on 28 per cent. of the area that can be used; and it has a mean density of 2·2 persons to the square mile. Hence, as was said above, most tropical countries are thinly peopled. Furthermore, their inhabitants are generally backward in civilization, being either mere food gatherers living on the spontaneous produce of the wild flora and fauna or else cultivators who have remained at a rudimentary stage of agricultural technique. They used to have no knowledge of writing, and their achievements in the intellectual sphere are very modest. These two outstanding features of mankind in the tropics are closely connected. Dense populations are generally possessed of a higher civilization, because they have been able to solve the economic, technical, social, and political problems raised by greater density. The hot, wet parts of Asia have a density of 171 persons to the square mile and contain one-quarter of mankind on 8 per cent. of the earth's exploitable surface. The people stand far higher on the scale of civilization than other tropical peoples. Tropical Asia is therefore a different world and deserves special study.[1] It may be that the physical conditions influencing man's use of Nature are different or that, on the contrary, the civilizations themselves may be responsible for the special character of the region.

The 3 million square miles of tropical Asia are in contrast with the 11½ million square miles of the rest of the hot, wet belt. The main features of the latter, sparse population and backward civilization, must be explained first of all. They are of such general occurrence that attempts have often been made to attribute them to the direct action of the climate, *i.e.* to the meteorological conditions; and it has been thought that the hot, damp climate must limit man's physical and mental activity. But endless research has brought no conclusive views on the matter[2] and has thrown no light on the thorny question of the direct influence of climate on man. The hot, wet regions of Asia with their teeming populations and high civilizations prove that it would be wise not to be positive in our conclusions. But unhealthiness on the one hand and poverty and instability of the various types of soil on the other are climatic effects which in

[1] See below, pp. 99–112.
[2] Sorre has summarized them in *Les fondements biologiques de la géographie humaine*. Paris, Colin, 1943.

their turn have a visible and profound influence on man. At certain stages in the development of technique and civilization unhealthiness and the nature of tropical soils explain the small numbers of the population, the low standard of life, and the cultural stagnation. Agriculture, pastoral life, and the exploitation of the forests as well as the number and health of the people depend on these two great factors which are themselves linked with the climate.

CHAPTER 2

UNHEALTHINESS OF THE HOT, WET REGIONS

COUNTRIES in the tropics are less healthy than those in the temperate belt. Most of the diseases of temperate lands are rife in hot, wet countries, whilst certain terrible endemic and epidemic tropical diseases are unknown in our latitudes. In physical and mental activity and in the reproduction of his kind, man is restricted in the tropics by serious maladies whose existence is entirely due to the hot, damp climate. We who live in temperate lands find it difficult to realize how baneful Nature can be to man or to understand that in unreclaimed regions water may swarm with dangerous germs, myriads of blood-sucking insects may inject deadly microbes into the human body, and the very soil may be harmful to the touch.

Man is not the only victim of the unhealthiness of the tropics. Close examination of animals in hot, wet regions shows that they are attacked by serious diseases of various kinds. For instance, the gibbon is in a poor state of health in Siam and is found to be infested with parasites.[1] Cattle are subject to trypanosomiasis in equatorial Africa; sheep cannot live in hot, wet regions; and the huge animal burial places found in Africa are probably due to trypanosomiatic diseases.

This unhealthiness is connected with the climate. The steady, high temperature, the humidity of the air, the many water surfaces fed by the rains are necessary for the continued existence of pathogenetic complexes in which man, an insect, and a microbe are closely associated.

Malaria is the most widespread of tropical diseases. Though it occurs in certain temperate regions, its main spheres of action are in the hot, wet belt. It attacks something like one-third of the human race, but in practice all the inhabitants of the hot, wet belt may be considered to be more or less infected.[2] Malaria weakens those whom it attacks, for the bouts of fever sap their physical strength and make them unfit for sustained effort. Hence, agriculture does not receive all the care it needs, and the food supply is thereby affected. In this

---

[1] See the account of researches by M. Schultz of Baltimore in *L'Anthropologie*, 1939, p. 211. It may console mankind to know that the gibbons suffered from abscesses on their teeth. Besides, they were found to have many malformations, hernias, atrophied arms, extra fingers, etc.

[2] The densely peopled regions of tropical Asia present special conditions; see below, p. 101.

way a vicious circle is formed. Weakened by insufficient nourishment, the system offers small resistance to infection[1] and cannot provide the effort required to produce an adequate supply of food. The malarial patient knows quite well that a bout of fever may be the unpleasant reward for hard work. In a period of six months a hundred workmen from a healthy district suffered the following casualties in unhealthy road work in French Indo-China:—between 15 and 25 men were eliminated by death or evacuation; those remaining had, owing to temporary indisposition, lost 25 per cent. of their capacity for work; and the capacity for work of the group had fallen off by 50 per cent. It is estimated that in India between 1901 and 1931 malaria was the direct cause of death of 30 million persons. Indirectly, by furthering the action of other diseases, it caused even more deaths. But the most serious fact perhaps is that one death from malaria corresponds to at least 2,000 days of illness.

Malaria carries off a great many infants who are infected from birth. It may kill adults through general debility, pernicious and cerebral attacks, and blackwater fever; and it prepares the way for the development of other diseases. It may take epidemic form and ravage districts previously little affected. In the years 1931 to 1935 Ceylon was hard hit, more than 100,000 persons dying of malaria, and the consumption of quinine rose to three tons a month.

Malaria normally requires heat and standing water. The hæmatozoa in the body of the anopheles die if they are subjected to temperatures below 60° F. several nights running, and the mosquito likes heat for itself and its larvæ. The latter, which develop in water, have precise requirements which differ according to species. Certain of them prefer shady water; others, more numerous, favour running water warmed by the sun. In Serra do Mar in Brazil certain anopheles even go so far as to find for their larvæ little pools of water which collect in the leaf-bunches of epiphytic Bromeliaceæ. Thus, owing to the myriads of these tiny hanging aquaria, certain trees being able to carry as many as three thousand of the species of Bromeliaceæ called *gravata* in Brazil, what may be termed Bromeliacean malaria is started. Hence, throughout the area covered by the hot, wet regions the anopheles finds conditions favouring its rapid multiplication.

The seriousness of malaria varies with the species of anopheles carriers. Whilst *Anopheles gambiæ* and *funestus* are fiercely hostile

---

[1] The malaria epidemic which ravaged Ceylon in 1933–4 was fomented by a famine due to drought and already raging. The official report on the epidemic states: 'Even if the population had been well fed and prosperous, there would have been a malaria epidemic, but the vicious circle in which malaria and physical weakness mutually favour each other would not have been established, the death-rate would have been lower, convalescence would have been quicker, and there would have been fewer relapses.'

to man in Africa, and whilst in Southeast Asia *A. minimus, maculatus*, and *umbrosus* are no less deadly, Brazil has the relative good fortune to owe its malaria mainly to *A. darlingi*, a creature that is somewhat less to be feared, owing to the habits of the adult and the peculiar requirements of the larvæ.

Undoubtedly, malaria is largely responsible for the poor health, small numbers, absence of enthusiasm for work, stationary demographic character, and backwardness of tropical peoples. The decadence of certain districts in the Mediterranean at the end of the Roman Empire has been attributed to the spread of malaria due ultimately to political troubles which disorganized the drainage system. The disease is far more able to check the development of population in hot, wet lands, where marsh fever rages virulently all the time. The depopulation of the district of Anuradhapura in northern Ceylon was preceded by political troubles which ruined the network of irrigation canals and the ricefield system, and so helped the countryside to run wild and malaria to develop. If the northern borders of Angkor in Cambodia are almost deserted today, the causes for it are much the same. The former occupation of the area is proved by irrigation dams. But the work was ruined and the district abandoned owing to Siamese invasions, after which it became infested with malaria. This terrible disease can only be checked by drainage operations undertaken purposely or incidentally. Examples of such operations will be given later.[1]

Intestinal diseases also contribute largely to weakening man in the tropics. The intestine of an inhabitant of Yucatan, when seen under a microscope, is a terrible 'museum of horrors,'[2] in which such a large number of organisms is found that immunological prophylaxis seems to offer no remedy. Improvement in sanitation would alone be effective. So common are intestinal diseases in the country that the Mayas have little fear of them; and it would take a long time to teach this people hygienic habits. The number of deaths due to intestinal diseases is certainly astonishing, but it is even more surprising that in such conditions man can survive the age of infancy.[3]

Tropical Africa offers an almost complete collection of intestinal diseases, especially amœbic and bacillary dysentery, which are serious, even deadly, and at the very least extremely weakening; maladies contracted by drinking water or eating raw vegetables; and ankylostomiasis, which is due to worms whose larvæ penetrate into the human body through the skin of the foot, and so is caught by

[1] See below, pp. 100–103 and 134.
[2] See a medical report published in the *Geog. Review*, 1935, p. 346.
[3] Similarly, when R. E. Crist studied the population of the middle São Francisco River in Brazil he thought it wonderful that so many of the inhabitants reached adult age. (*Geog. Review*, 1944, p. 605.)

mere contact with the soil. The settlement of a number of hook-worms in the duodenum brings on anæmia through intestinal disorders and much hæmorrhage. Now, the investigation of hookworms has led to positive results in 50 per cent. of the cases in the Senegal, in 87 per cent. of those in French Guinea, and in 74 per cent. of those on the Ivory Coast.

Dysentery and ankylostomiasis are the principal intestinal diseases, but other sicknesses of less importance make up a formidable array —tape-worms of various species and intestinal bilharziasis which is contracted in bathing. Altogether, anyone who harbours plasmodia in his blood and a rich collection of amœbæ and dysenteric bacilli, hookworms, tape-worms, schistosomes of bilharziasis, and various other parasites in his intestines—as do most of those who dwell in the hot, wet regions—must certainly be debilitated, unfit for hard physical work, and incapable of great mental effort.

In certain conditions of the environment intestinal diseases may be more virulent than malaria. This is the case in Yucatan, which, being composed of a block of Pliocene limestone, has no surface drainage.[1] Ground water rarely comes to the surface, and then only at the bottom of certain *dolines* in ponds called *Cenotes*. The climate is sub-arid, with a severe dry season and a wet season which brings only thirty-one inches of rain. These conditions do not exclude malaria, but restrict its ravages, making it less widespread here than in the rainier districts to the south, like the Guatemaltecan province of Petén. On the other hand, intestinal diseases have become terribly prevalent. Perhaps this is due to the fact that the ground water is infected and that in this limestone country the streams are not filtered, but circulate easily through a widely meshed network of channels.

Other diseases peculiar to warm latitudes overwhelm man in the tropics. Bilharziasis of the bladder is especially deadly in Africa, and kala-azar causes considerable havoc in India. Man's vitality is further sapped by filarial diseases, elephantiasis, Guinea worm (dracontiasis), transient Calabar œdema, and onchocerciasis. This last affection, which sometimes causes blindness, is transmitted by sand-flies whose bite is enough to make it disagreeable to stay in some parts of Uganda. The N'Ghan tribe in the Bavule district of the Ivory Coast owes its name to the general lameness caused by the presence of Guinea worm in the lower limbs. Yaws is endemic on the coasts of the Gulf of Guinea. This is a disease which is suspected of being a cause of the terrible deformity of the bones known as goundou, or anakhrë, and is often fatal. Tropical ulcers, leishmaniasis,

---

[1] *The Peninsula of Yucatan*, by G. C. Shattuck and various collaborators, Carnegie Institute Publication, No. 431.

and relapsing fevers complete this short list, the horror of which is increased by sleeping sickness and yellow fever, both deserving of special notice. Undernourishment partly explains this host of scourges,[1] but the main responsibility rests with the climate. Of course, no mention is made here of diseases of the temperate belt which are widespread in the tropics.[2]

Yellow fever is confined to hot countries, because both the virus and the insects that carry it require a high temperature. It was thought that in Africa the disease was restricted to active endemic centres on the Gulf of Guinea, but recent research has revealed that in a dormant form it reaches as far as Uganda. Perhaps man is indispensable for the survival of the virus, which must have insect and man as successive hosts. In other words, a healthy man who settles in a hot, wet country which was absolutely uninhabited cannot catch yellow fever in spite of an abundance of carrier-insects. The same is true of many other tropical diseases, and this fact has its effect on the colonization of hot countries. Such regions are colonized with relative ease if they are quite uninhabited and if the immigrants are healthy; but the enterprise becomes risky if they are already inhabited, that is, if they contain many carriers of the virus. But in Brazil *Rhesus* monkeys are infected with the same kind of yellow fever as men are. Who in this case was originally responsible, man or monkey?

Sleeping sickness is peculiar to tropical Africa, though there is a kind of trypanosomiasis in America. The limits of the tsetse infected regions are perhaps the best that can be given for the disease in hot, wet Africa. The form caused by *Trypanosoma rhodesiense*, which is the most serious, is perhaps identical with the horse disease due to *T. brucei*. Sleeping sickness causes many deaths and physically and mentally weakens the persons it affects. Now, it was observed in the Cameroons in 1923 that 42 per cent. of the population of the district of Akonolinga were infected, and in the Nupe district in Nigeria it was found in 1936 that the percentage was as high as 70. Sleeping sickness has grown worse in Africa south of the Sahara owing to the movement of population. As there are many root-stocks from which the micro-organisms of the disease spring, an individual accustomed to one local stock may be stricken to death if he moves into districts in which other stocks flourish. Sleeping sickness, like many other

---

[1] See below, p. 65 ff.

[2] This list of tropical diseases does not pretend to be complete. It could easily be lengthened by the addition of pyomyositis (muscular suppuration due to a *Pasteurella* or a *Micrococcus* and occurring in the upper Senegal and upper Niger) and of porocephalosis (a parasitic disease caused by porocephales, Arachnida which infest the windpipe and lungs of snakes). Cp. *L'œuvre des Pastoriens en Afrique noire* by Surgeon-General C. Mathis, pub. Presses Universitaires, Paris, 1946. See pp. 352 and 433. Note also Frambœsia, a disease caused by spirochætes.

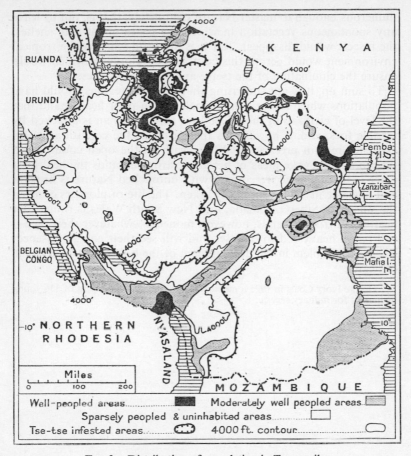

FIG. 3. Distribution of population in Tanganyika

(After C. Gillman, 'A Population Map of Tanganyika Territory,' in *Geog. Review*, 1936, and E. Weigt, 'Schlafkrankheitsbekampfung in Tanganyika,' in *Petermanns G. Mitteilungen*, 1938)

tropical diseases, and malaria in particular, is a disease proper to uncivilized or half-civilized countries. The tsetse fly, which is very exacting as regards conditions of temperature and humidity, finds the necessary shelter in uncleared forest or woodland. In other words, the complete 'humanization' of a district involves the complete disappearance of the tsetse.[1] In Tanganyika[2] the tsetse is not responsible for the low density of population; rather, it is the low density that causes the abundance of the pest. If the population were

[1] See below, p. 131, for methods of fighting sleeping sickness.
[2] See Gillman, *Geog. Review*, 1936, p. 354.

numerous enough to master Nature completely, that is, not to leave any spontaneous vegetation in which the tsetse might take shelter, the insects would disappear. But it is doubtful whether the tropical environment would permit this complete development which would ensure the elimination of the tsetse and sleeping sickness.

To sum up, it is not surprising that hot, wet regions should have populations which are generally small and in poor health[1] and that the level of civilization should be low, for there man is attacked by terrible foes, and, if he survives their attacks, the conditions of his existence remain precarious. Whilst with us the open country and the woodland evoke ideas of health, in tropical lands the healthiest place is the town, where contact with untouched Nature is broken, and hygienic measures are easily taken. The life of pioneers clearing the wastes of Siberia, Canada, and New South Wales is rough, but healthy; in tropical lands, however, pioneers—whatever their race—will pay a heavy toll to disease, and will see their energy lessened. The main problem in the development of the hot, wet regions is one of health.

[1] On the Ivory Coast in 1925 a medical board passed only 40 out of 336 young men as fit for military service.

CHAPTER 3

TROPICAL SOILS

TROPICAL soils are poorer and more fragile than those of temperate regions. Great care is needed in using them, if their further impoverishment and destruction are to be avoided. These conditions give tropical agriculture a precarious character which is absent from the temperate belt, except in sub-arid regions where the agents of erosion are on the look-out for ground that has been cleared.

Ill-informed writers are fond of calling to mind 'the inexhaustible wealth' of tropical soils which, they suppose, nourish the irresistible luxuriance of the equatorial forest. This forest is supposed to be an 'invincible' obstacle to man, because it is said to grow up again as fast as it is cut down. Overwhelmed by the forest, man is thought to be deprived of air and light—which does not prevent him from having a black or dark-coloured skin. This touching picture is inaccurate.[1]

Forests in the hot belt are rarely virgin, but more often secondary, that is, forest which has grown again after being cleared by man. They have no more vitality than the temperate forest, because they usually grow in very poor soil. The fertility of Trinidad is a myth based on the fine appearance of the forest.[2] But equatorial forest may thrive exceedingly on infertile soil. In fact, the finest forests in Trinidad, forests of *Mora excelsa benth.*, grow in sterile sands. The

[1] Too much stress has often been laid on the barrier presented by 'virgin' forest to human activity. The central portion of the Congo basin, which is occupied by equatorial forest, is in fact more sparsely peopled than the peripheral territory where the forest thins out and gives way to savana (see below, p. 85). But many examples prove that numerous communities, like the Ibo people in Southern Nigeria (see below, p. 87), have developed on areas previously occupied by equatorial forest. It must, however, be agreed that for primitive peoples, who have no other agricultural system than that of clearing the ground by fire and allowing the fallow to return to forest, the true equatorial forest is a serious obstacle. It is difficult to fell; and the need to clear a fresh area of forest every year is exhausting for people who are in poor health and possess rudimentary implements. Fire, which is the tropical cultivator's best tool, is of irregular and problematical assistance in a really equatorial climate.

Now, it may be asked whether the labour of continuously tilling fields is not as toilsome as, or even more laborious than, that of clearing away the forest. Besides, the people who grow regular crops, whether in flooded paddy-fields or plantations of trees, are not hindered by the resistance of the equatorial forest to fire; and areas of equatorial climate without a dry season are not extensive.

Altogether, the influence of the forest on the human geography of hot countries has not seemed sufficiently clear to warrant special treatment. See what is said below, pp. 75–6, concerning the economic value of tropical forest.

[2] J. S. Beard: *Land Utilisation Survey of Trinidad, Farm and Forest* (Ibadan), Dec. 1941, p. 133.

13

'virgin' forest demands scarcely anything from the soil and lives in a state of equilibrium. Organic matter fallen from the trees constitutes the humus, and everything that the forest produces goes back to the forest. Clearing causes unpleasant surprise, for instead of deep humus sand is found, and the forest may have the greatest difficulty in growing up again once man's exploitation has exposed the underlying sand. Expanses of brushwood in Trinidad are eloquent in this respect. Similarly, in Belgian Congo the sandy beds at Lubilash bear a fine open forest in their original state; but on being cleared the soil rapidly becomes exhausted.

Hence, it must not be inferred from the luxuriance of the vegetation that the soil is rich in hot, wet lands. Besides, analysis shows that, apart from rare exceptions, tropical soils are very poor in assimilable bases and phosphorus and ill supplied with humus. The deficiencies are such that soils of similar composition would be barren in a temperate climate. A piece of cultivated land of average quality on the delta of the Tongking which yields two crops of rice a year contains the following elements making for fertility:—lime, less than 5 per thousand; magnesia, less than 2 per thousand (there is no possible comparison with temperate soils, which are basic and not acid); potash, less than $0 \cdot 1$ per thousand (in temperate lands soil with less than $0 \cdot 5$ per thousand is not cultivable)[1]; phosphoric acid, less than $0 \cdot 1$ per thousand (in temperate lands soil with less than $0 \cdot 2$ per thousand is not cultivable). The content of humus and nitrogen will be examined later.[2] According to J. Baeyens, the pedologist,[3] much of the land occupied by profitable plantations in the lower Congo valley would, if transported to Belgium, be heath or utterly barren moorland.

So great is their poverty in bases that tropical soils are acid, a condition unfavourable to good use of the humus. But cultivated tropical plants are adapted to acid conditions, and tropical agriculture is satisfied with the poorest soils, provided that they have a suitable physical texture, that is to say, that they are sufficiently friable.

The poverty of tropical soils is often revealed quite unexpectedly by a yield inferior to that of temperate soils. In spite of the slight differences in conditions and of adjustments which further examination would not fail to render necessary, the facts given in the table below afford a suggestive comparison.[4]

[1] G. Wiegner: *Anleitung zum Quantitativen Agrikultur-Chemischen Praktikum*, Berlin, 1926.
[2] See below, p. 17.
[3] J. Baeyens: *Les sols de l'Afrique centrale, spécialement du Congo belge*, vol. I; *Le Bas-Congo*, pub. by I.N.E.A.C., Brussels, Supplement No. 6, 1938, p. 22.
[4] Taken from Van Hall, Report of the Internat. Geog. Congress at Amsterdam, 1938, *Colonial Geography*, pp. 125-30.

AVERAGE YIELD OF RICE PER ACRE 1926/27–1930/31.

Temperate countries	Bushels per acre	Tropical countries	Bushels per acre
Spain .	187	Sierra Leone .	62
Italy .	122	Siam . .	50
Japan .	107	Indonesia .	47
United States	65	Brazil . .	44
Korea .	56	India . .	41
		Philippines .	35
		Malaya .	35
		Madagascar .	35
		French Indo-China	32

As will be seen, tropical countries give a lower yield. The validity of the comparison might be contested, for some of the figures are doubtful. In particular, the yield in Indo-China is very probably greater than the official figure. Besides, it is doubtful whether the yield obtained from small, well-chosen temperate ricefields can fairly be compared with that of tropical paddy-fields, which is calculated on immense areas representing sometimes nearly the whole of the cultivable land. But a comparison between wheat and rice also shows the inferiority of the tropics. And swamp rice gives the best yield of all tropical cereals. Upland rice, sorghum, and eleusine are far less profitable. In Indonesia, where the climate is favourable and the fertility of the soil generally above the average for the tropics, upland rice yields only 800 lb. to the acre, as against 1,450 lb. yielded by swamp rice. The comparison of wheat and rice gives the following results:—

	Yield per acre	Protein Content	Carbo-hydrate Content	Fats
	Bushels	Bushels	Bushels	Bushels
Wheat (averages for Europe and U.S.A.) . .	53·64	5·9	37·55	0·87
Rice (average of seven main producing tropical countries) .	44·70	2·15	24·67	0·72

Maize is grown in both tropical and temperate regions. The following table gives a comparison of the yield in the two regions:—

Temperate countries	Bushels per acre	Tropical countries	Bushels per acre
Argentine .	62·58	Brazil . .	29·80
Manchuria	50·66	Belgian Congo	29·80
U.S.A. .	47·68	Indonesia .	29·80
Italy . .	47·68	India . .	25·82
Hungary	44·70	Mexico . .	17·88
Spain .	44·70		
France .	38·74		
Romania .	32·78		
Bulgaria .	32·78		

Hence, the lower yield in tropical countries seems to be definitely proved. To be completely valid, however, the comparison should be extended to include root-crops. The carbohydrate content of cassava, yams, and sweet potatoes on the one hand and of potatoes on the other is much greater than that of cereals. But the statistical data available for tropical root-crops are far from sufficient.

Why are tropical soils, with rare exceptions, so infertile? They are often deep, for the bedrock may have decomposed to a depth of several scores of feet.[1] But the soluble matter, bases and nitrates, is soon carried away by percolating water aided by the high temperature, the presence of carbonic acid and nitric acid, and by countless bacteria. It should be remembered that the warmer the water and the greater its acidity, the higher becomes its coefficient of electrolytic dissociation. Chemical and bio-chemical action goes so deep that the silicates are decomposed. Contrary to what takes place in our climate, the silica is dissolved and carried off by the water.

The bases are all the more quickly leached out because they are not retained by the 'adsorbent' complex which would be formed by a rich proportion of organic matter. Tropical soils are poor in humus. Even in the forest humus blackens the soil to a depth of only a few inches. In dense forests the quantity of organic matter deposited is considerable and has been estimated in Yangambi in Belgian

[1] M. Revert has kindly informed the author that in Martinique the whole area devastated by the eruption of Morne Pelée which destroyed the town of St. Pierre in 1902 was covered with brushwood in 1927, as was also the lava spine. This is proof of the rapid decomposition of rock in a moist tropical climate, and in the instance mentioned it was an advantage.

1. A mosquito haunt. A mangrove swamp through which the River Pachu runs on the island of Choiseul in the Solomons. Note the roots of the mangroves and the stillness of the water.

2. Malaria control. Cleaning the banks of the Milk River so as to remove mosquito-breeding pools.

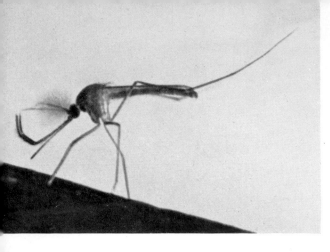

3. *Anopheles quadrimaculatus* with its proboscis plunged into a man's arm.

4. A tsetse fly (*Glossina palpalis*).

5. A Madrasi boy suffering from elephantiasis ("Barbados leg").

Congo at between twenty and twenty-five tons of leaves, twigs, lianas, and branches per annum per acre.[1] But in these forests the deposits do not enrich the soil, for they are offset by equivalent losses, with the result that the soil contains at most 1·8 per cent. of humus, whilst fertile soil in temperate regions often contains more than 10 per cent.

The explanation is that organic matter is quickly decomposed and reduced to the condition of soluble minerals and easily lost to the soil. First of all, it is broken down by countless insects, the most active of which are termites.[2] (See Photo. 9.) Thus, the way is prepared for the action of micro-organisms which destroy humus. The number and activity of the micro-organisms have been proved by experiments made in Java to be increased by heat. The humus content of the surface-layer of the soil was shown to rise from 5 per cent. at an altitude of 1,000 feet above sea level and a mean annual temperature of 76° F. to 14 per cent. at an altitude of 3,250 feet and a mean temperature of 68° F. The organic nitrogen is soon transformed into nitrates which, being in too great a quantity for the needs of the forest trees, are dissolved by the water and finally lost. This is one of the great differences between the tropics and the temperate belt; for, whilst temperate agriculture must overcome the slow rate at which organic nitrogen places itself at the disposal of plants, tropical agriculture must, on the contrary, worry over the waste of nitrogen. The loss of nitrogen is reckoned at between 60 and 70 lb. per acre per annum in the loams of temperate regions and at between 170 and 270 lb. in hot, wet lands. A rise in temperature favours the loss of nitrogen. Above 79° F. a rise of one degree in the temperature of the soil leads to an increased loss of humic nitrogen amounting to between 15 and 25 lb. per acre per annum, which is equivalent to between 100 and 125 lb. of sulphate of ammonia.

It is easy to verify the fact that an application of manure in the tropics makes its effect felt for far less time than in the temperate regions: a few months only, instead of two or three years. Roots left in soil cleared for cultivation disappear far more quickly in tropical lands.

In such conditions very fertile tropical soils will always be recent

[1] A. Beirnaert: *La Technique culturale sous l'Équateur,* I. *Influence de la culture sur les réserves en humus et en azote des terres équatoriales,* pub. I.N.E.A.C., Technical Series, No. 6, 1941, p. 12.

[2] The effect produced by termites is various. Though termites are great destroyers of organic matter and humus (for many termites feed on humus) it is agreed, on the other hand, that termitaries are often more fertile than the soil on which they stand. On the light, sandy soil of eastern Siam termitaries give soil that is heavier, more clayey, and neutral or basic, whilst the natural soil is acid. Rich crops of cotton, tobacco, mulberry, beans, pine-apples, or sugar cane may flourish on termitary soils. (R. L. Pendleton: in *Geog. Review,* 1942, p. 323.)

soils which have not had time to become poor, such as those derived from clearing the forest (though these are not certain to keep their fertility for long); present-day fluvial alluvium, especially if it comes from non-tropical regions, *e.g.* recent alluvium from the Red River in Tongking, the Mekong, or the Ganges; recent marine alluvium like that on the shores of the Gulf of Guinea; soils due to very recent basic volcanic ash, as in eastern Java. Fluvial alluvium of the early Quaternary epoch is generally infertile in tropical lands.

The equatorial forest does not increase the quantity of humus, but maintains it. If the forest is destroyed, the soil no longer receives the organic matter indispensable for making humus, whilst the processes by which the humus is decomposed continue to act and are even accelerated because lack of cover makes the temperature of the soil rise. Whilst the surface-layer of soil does not exceed 77° or 79° F. under forest, it may reach 104° F. after the bush has been cleared away. Now, the rate at which humus (and organic nitrogen) deteriorates increases with the temperature.[1]

It should be added that bare soil is subject to great alterations in dryness and damp, and the alternate penetration of air and water into the macropores of the soil is harmful to it. What happens is that the water drives out the carbon dioxide before being replaced by air. Thus, the oxygen is continually being renewed, which is favourable to the combustion of the humus during the midday heat, and this combustion adds to the effect of bacteria. Turning up the soil with the hoe as well as with the plough aggravates the situation still further by favouring a rise in temperature.

The impoverishment of the soil in humus results in weakening the 'adsorbent' complex. Hence, the bases are no longer retained, and the soil is thereby further impoverished. In fact, humus plays an essential part in the complex because it has a capacity for 'adsorption' greater than that of clay and because in hot countries clays are more or less lateritic and have in that way lost a good deal of their capacity for 'adsorption.'

Percolating water leaches the soil by removing the bases and nitrates. Now, percolation is greater in bare soil than under forest. Evaporation from bare soil between the Equator and latitude 10° has been estimated at about 1,000 mm. (40 in.), whilst a dense

---

[1] According to E. C. J. Mohr, who is quoted by Baeyens on p. 101 of the work mentioned above on p. 14, n. 3, when the temperature of the soil remains about 77° F. equilibrium is established in tropical regions between the production of green matter and its mineralization. Below that temperature an accumulation of humus takes place; above it, humic matter gradually disappears. In fact, the optimum of assimilation of chlorophyll occurs between 68° F. and 77° F., and the optimum of activity of microbes between 86° and 95° F.

vegetable cover transpires at least 1,500 mm. (60 in.). Consequently, there is far more water to percolate in bare ground than under forest. The greater the percolation, the more active the leaching. The process will be accelerated by the impoverishment of the soil, since soil which is rich in humus can hold more water than poor soil. The removal of the humus will therefore assist percolation and the surface run-off at the same time.

For climatic reasons tropical soils are poor and tend to become poorer quickly. This would not be so bad if the soil remained in its place and kept a friable structure favourable to agriculture. But tropical soils are threatened with erosion and lateritization, the latter tendency being peculiar to hot, wet lands. Soil erosion is universal, but in tropical regions it assumes a very violent form. The aridity of bare soil exposes it helplessly to wind-erosion in the dry season and to the attacks of tremendous downpours at the beginning of the rainy season.

Soil erosion does not develop its full force unless the soil has been deprived of its natural forest protection. Strictly speaking, a good mantle of savana grass may protect the earth, but fire destroys this protection every year. Hence, man always appears as the root cause of soil erosion.[1] The mildest form of erosion (sheet erosion) occurs when the run-off is spread out over very gentle gradients. Even so, the water carries off the finest particles—that is, the most fertile— without leaving any noticeable trace, and the lower ground is slowly enriched at the expense of the higher. On steeper slopes which are not protected by vegetation the run-off acts more vigorously. The soil is no longer retained by the vegetation; besides, the absence of the latter reduces the amount of organic matter in the soil, which, being deprived of humus, absorbs water less readily. So the effect of the run-off is aggravated all the more. As the run-off removes the fine particles of humus and clay first, the soil on the higher ground becomes less and less capable of absorbing water, and so the effects of the run-off reinforce the run-off. Finally, when the drainage system becomes settled, the water carves the surface into branching gullies. In the end the soil is destroyed, and wide expanses become useless. The form taken by tropical agriculture is mainly due to the

[1] A few figures will give an accurate idea of the effects of the destruction of forests. In the Pabbi Hills in the Punjab Maclagan Gorrie reported at the International Geographical Congress at Amsterdam in 1938 (see *Colonial Geography*, pp. 405–16) that during an average shower of rain the drainage from a slope covered with good forest amounted to 3·4 cu. yd. per second per sq. mi.; from a slope covered with a continuous mantle of bush 22·3 cu. yd.; from a slope covered with scattered bushes, 37·2 cu. yd; and from a slope rendered bare by over-grazing, 61 cu. yd. To the damage done by erosion are added those caused by the deposition of sediment on the alluvial fans of mountain torrents.

twin anxieties of avoiding the dangers of exhaustion and erosion of the soil.[1] Every act of imprudence is dearly paid for. For instance, in the inter-Andine zone of Ecuador between Loja and Cuenca 75 per cent. of the land once cultivated now lies abandoned owing to soil erosion.[2]

Lateritic soils are no less of a disadvantage. A good deal of the hot, wet regions is covered with soils which are highly lateritic or of pure laterite. Now, laterite is utterly infertile. Composed of hydroxide of iron and of aluminium in variable proportions, it contains no element which is assimilable by plants : no soluble matter, lime, potash, nitrogen, phosphoric acid, or humus. On the other hand, laterite is hostile to vegetation owing to its compact texture and impermeability. The lateritic crusts in Guinea (*bowal*) and Senegambia are absolutely useless.[3] (See Photos. 6–8.)

Even if it does not form such crusts, laterite bears no carpet of green when it appears in the open air, as it does on the *tampoketsa* in Madagascar or the *khoai* in western Bengal. Irrigation has no useful effect on the relatively friable laterites in Madagascar, except to transform them into a compact puddled clay, whilst it enables crops to be forced from the pure and almost sterile sand of the coast strip. Chemical manures seem harmful rather than effective, since they produce toxic soluble salts of alumina. As for farm manure, it may be used, but only in what amounts to pot cultivation, as when a Malgash peasant makes a hole in the laterite with his spade, fills it with manure, and plants in this. The Merinas and Betsileos build the walls of their huts and gardens of puddled laterite. Such walls are avoided for an indefinite time by vegetation, neither moss, nor fungus, nor any higher form of vegetation taking hold on it, though they succeed in growing on walls of baked brick. Malgash laterite is so completely impermeable that the peasants make store-pits for grain in it without further trouble than digging holes with their spades. Laterite, which is the result of pedological evolution occurring *in situ*, ends by being harder than many rocks. This fact is noticeable in certain Khmer ruins. The Khmers used to build their magnificent edifices of laterite, covering the laterite with a veneer of sandstone. Sandstone lends itself to carving, whilst laterite cannot be chiselled owing to its cellular structure. It has been found that sandstone is less resistant than laterite to the agents of erosion; *e.g.* in the temple of Ban Gu near Roi Esh in north-eastern Siam the sandstone base of a door-frame has been eroded by the salts which rise by capillary attraction during

---

[1] See below, p. 25.
[2] *Geog. Review*, 1944, p. 64.
[3] The curious phosphic laterites in the district of Thiès in Senegal owe it to their hardness that they have no more agricultural value than ordinary laterites.

the dry season, whilst the immediately adjacent laterite remains intact.[1]

On the whole, laterite is hostile to agriculture owing to its sterility and compactness. All tropical countries have not reached the same degree of lateritic 'suicide,' but when the evolution has advanced a considerable way, man is placed in very strange conditions. Madagascar, an island of red laterite, has a cultivable area of only 30,000 square miles out of a total area of 190,000 square miles. Laterite is perhaps not entirely responsible for the sterility of the useless 160,000 square miles, but all the same it occupies the greater part of the area.[2]

Laterite is a pedological leprosy which occurs only in hot, wet climates with an alternation of dry and rainy seasons. Heat and rain are needed for the soil to be leached of the bases which would prevent the formation of laterite, for the underlying rock to be attacked deeply, and for the silicates of alumina and iron to be decomposed. Thus, it is formed of hydroxide of alumina and iron, whilst the silica is dissolved and removed by spring water. In fact, laterite is formed at the expense of silicate rocks—but there are few rocks which do not contain silicates.

A dry season is needed for the water far below the surface to rise by capillary attraction to the surface and there evaporate. The water brings with it hydroxide of alumina and iron which forms laterite and lateritic cements. An equatorial climate, being without a dry season, is therefore less favourable to the formation of laterite than a tropical climate. Yet it seems that in a hot climate which is constantly rainy a somewhat imperfect kind of laterite forms at a great depth,[3] whilst lateritization comes nearer and nearer the surface as one approaches the desert belt. A map showing lateritic areas in West Africa north of the Equator might be drawn as follows: in the equatorial climate or in the subequatorial climate with two wet and two short dry seasons the solidified layer occurs at depths varying between 18 inches and 9 feet. The surface soil is not lateritic and will not be exhausted if it supports a forest. Between lat. 10° and lat. 14°. N. lateritic crusts are formed. When they appear on the surface, they are known as *bowal*; when they are covered by a layer of soil, this layer may support a forest. North of lat. 14° N. laterite crusts are no longer found, except in a fossil state; but it forms a pisolitic

[1] R. L. Pendleton: 'Laterite and its Structural Uses in Thailand and Cambodia,' *Geog. Review*, 1941, pp. 177–202.

[2] See Fig. 10, p. 62.

[3] According to that excellent observer, the late Scaetta, c.r. of the Académie des Sciences in Paris, Jan. 20, 1941; Jan. 27, 1941; Feb. 17, 1941. 'Les types climatiques de l'A.O.F.: leur rapport avec l'évolution du sol tropical,' in *La Météorologie*, Jan. 1939, pp. 39–48.

gravel which is no less fatal than laterite, for the gravel constitutes an insulating layer whose temperature excludes the hardiest plants.[1]

Man's activities aggravate the dangers of laterite and increase the rate of the process of lateritization. To begin with, erosion when started by negligent removal of the forest simply washes away the friable and relatively fertile soil which would otherwise cover the laterite and support forest or crops. Useful expanses have become dead areas in this way. The *khoai* in western Bengal, where the removal of the forests of *sal* (*Shorea robusta*) set erosion in motion, were probably formed thus.

So a ready-made crust of laterite appears at the surface; but then again lateritization is encouraged by man's destruction of the forest for the forest checks the formation of laterite in various ways. The trees supply plenty of organic matter and maintain a good proportion of humus in the soil; the action of capillary attraction is checked by the loosening of the soil; and the bases are retained through the absorbent capacity of humus. The forest slows down evaporation from the soil, because it keeps the soil temperature comparatively low; it ensures evaporation through the leaves and not through the soil, thanks to the water drunk in by the roots; and it reduces percolation and consequently leaching. Lastly, the forest may perhaps improve the composition of the soil by fixing atmospheric dust.

Laterite is a dead soil, a rock which does not decompose and on which chemical erosion has no effect. Areas whose surface is formed by laterite are worthless. Soils in which laterite is incompletely formed may be cultivated if they offer a good physical texture, as in certain gritty soils observed in the lower Congo valley;[2] but they are very poor nevertheless. They can, however, cause a further inconvenience which has been observed in Malaya.[3] Though the climate is rainy and the soil saturated, drinking water is hard to get, for the lateritic soil retains the water colloidally and does not allow it to seep into the wells.

Limestone rocks do not lend themselves to the formation of laterite, except through the intermediate stage of *terra rossa*. Nevertheless, the evolution of limestone in the hot, wet belts ends no less unfortunately than the lateritization of siliceous rocks. An extreme case of this hostility to man is found in the district of Ke Bang on the

[1] Laterite is associated not only with mineralogical and climatic conditions, but also with surface relief, for it forms on even surfaces. It is not found on steep slopes, but on plateaus and terraces. It is a characteristic formation on peneplains, that is, on very even surfaces caused by erosion during a long period of stability.

[2] J. Baeyens, *op. cit.*, above, p. 14, n. 3; *cp.* p. 18.

[3] E. H. G. Dobby, in *Geog. Review*, 1942, p. 219.

borders of Annam and Laos between lat. 17° and 18° N. Here the Uralo-Permian limestones are completely uninhabited over an area of from 2,000 to 2,300 square miles. There is not a single inhabitant in a district as big as a French department, although the rainfall is 60 inches a year and the altitude is moderate, rising no higher than 3,000 feet. But the relief consists of an infinite series of steep-sided little peaks criss-crossed with narrow cracks (*lapiés*). The peaks touch each other at their bases and give no room between them for flat-bottomed valleys or enclosed hollows filled with *terra rossa*. There are no streams, for the drainage percolates through the rock; nor is there any path, and one's progress is but an exhausting succession of ups and downs over rough rocks fortunately covered with trees on which the hand can find a hold.

Only a few clay-bottomed hollows on the borders are inhabited, and even so one reaches them only by a hazardous crossing by means of ladders over ramparts of limestone. The pigs and buffaloes in them have been carried thither in their owners' arms when quite young and cannot escape from these vertically-sided amphitheatres.

To explain this kind of relief certain special conditions must be taken into account. The very hard limestone has been greatly folded and has been exposed for a long time to the action of erosion. The fact remains, nevertheless, that this type of relief which is utterly hostile to man has been caused by the tropical climate with its warm,[1] heavy rain laden with nitric acid. The Ke Bang district is the world's largest expanse of desert exclusively connected with the nature of the rock and with the relief—a low relief at that. The same facts are found again, though on smaller areas, in other parts of French Indo-China, northern Siam, eastern Burma, in the *magotes* of the Guaniguanico Hills in Cuba,[2] in the islands of Japan and Waigeu,[3] in the neighbourhood of Coban in the district of Alta Verapaz in Guatemala, and elsewhere. Java's Duizendgebergte ('Thousand Mountains') are a milder form of the same type of landscape. In temperate lands limestone never gives rise to forms so hostile to man at a low altitude.

Horizontal sandstones, which occupy vast areas in the hot, wet belt, make for quiet landscapes. But the sandy soils which form their surface are of little use, even when they do not develop laterite. The enormous area of these continental sandstones is a curse of tropical lands.

---

[1] Owing to the higher temperature the water is more 'ionized' and consequently contains more acid 'ions.' The greater acidity of the water increases its power of attacking limestones as well as other minerals.

[2] H. H. Bennett: 'Some Geographic Aspects of Cuban Soils,' in *Geog. Review*, 1928, pp. 62–82.

[3] L. E. Cheesman: 'Two Unexplored Islands of Dutch New Guinea,' in the *Geographical Journal*, 1940, I, pp. 208–17.

On the whole, tropical soils are less favourable to man than temperate soils, which are richer and more stable. A study of the composition of the two types of soils always ends in the establishment of the overwhelming superiority of the temperate over the tropical in fertile chemical elements. This superiority is due to the climate, tropical conditions being especially favourable to the destruction of humus, the leaching away of the bases, and to lateritization. Owing to these special conditions, man has not generally secured control of the arable soil in the tropics. It is therefore not surprising that tropical peoples are often few in number and have not built up higher civilizations of their own. Civilization can be developed only if it rests on a firm control of the soil, and this control is secured with more difficulty in the tropics than in the temperate belt.

CHAPTER 4

THE CHARACTERISTIC AGRICULTURE
OF THE TROPICS

TROPICAL soils impose severe conditions on agriculture. Man's response must be skilful if he wishes to avoid losing the soil. In all hot, wet regions the cultivator has found the same solutions for the problems set him by the soil. Universality in space goes hand in hand with universality in time. Europeans in Brazil employed the same methods as the Amerindians, the Africans (see Figs. 4 and 5, pp. 36–7), the Indonesians, or the Melanesians. The object is to produce carbohydrates, which are the basis of human food, by means of unirrigated food-crops. The technique is everywhere the same. Patches of land are cleared of vegetation by burning and after being used for a crop or two are abandoned and allowed to return to forest again for a long while. The system may briefly be termed *ray* (French Indo-China), *caingin* (Philippines), *milpa* (Mexico), *coamile* (Mexico), *conuco* (Venezuela), *ladang* (Java), *roça* (Brazil), and *masole* (Belgian Congo).

The cultivator marks out a piece of the forest, choosing it for its special fertility. This quality is indicated by certain plants. In Brazil preference is given to land in which grow *padroes*, or tree-guides, especially *Gallesia gorasema*. In the Cameroons the Bulus like soils which favour *Thaumatococcus Danieli* and *Cassia Alata*. In Dahomey the cultivator tastes a pinch of soil to know if it is fertile.

Then the trees are felled and the bush cleared away. The biggest trees may be spared, for they are useful for fixing the soil and protecting it from erosion; or it may be thought sufficient to kill them by ring-barking. Usually the trees are felled about six feet from the ground, because in hot lands trees generally have buttresses which widen their bases, and so to cut them off at ground-level would be labour lost. In consequence of all this, the ground remains bristling with trunks and presents a hirsute appearance.

As the natural vegetation would not burn without it, clearing is necessary. When the Light and Power Co. wished to destroy the forest which was to be flooded by their dams in the State of São Paulo, they had to spray it with mineral oil in order to burn it, as they did not wish to go to the expense of felling the trees.[1]

[1] P. Deffontaines in *Bull. de la Société de Géographie de Lille*, 1939, p. 58.

When the trees and branches are dry, they are burnt.[1] At the end of the dry season columns of smoke rising in every direction indicate the work of clearing. Destruction by fire is easier than any other method when one's only implements are the hoe and an inadequate axe.[2] If necessary, some precautions are taken to prevent the fire from spreading to the rest of the forest, but this is generally unnecessary, since the rain-forest contains little combustible material. The soil is enriched with ashes from the fire. To secure greater fertility the Bantus in Rhodesia and Nyasaland pile up on the chosen patch branches collected from all around; and in doing this they remove the vegetation from an area six or eight times larger than that of the patch. The havoc caused by their *chitimene* is therefore considerable, though it is less than it might be, since the Bantus are satisfied to use the boughs and do not fell the trunks, so that the trees are able to sprout again. Climbing the trees to cut off the branches is a sport that calls for plenty of pluck. The men display great rivalry and daring; and accidents are frequent. The women pile up the branches to form a layer about ten feet high.[3]

The firing of the patch cleared is an operation of dubious value, if the effects are carefully weighed. It leaves fertile ashes, but destroys between 250 and 450 tons per acre of organic matter which would have been more profitable in the form of timber, firewood, wood-pulp, leaf manure, and products from the distillation of wood. Betweeen 600 and 900 lb. of nitrogen per acre go up in smoke; the potash is reduced to a very soluble form of carbonate which is leached away by the first showers; and the humus and bacteria are destroyed.[4]   From previous measurements taken at Yangambi in Belgian Congo it was found that a hectare of primary forest produced the following quantities of organic matter: 30 tons of litter and dead wood, 39 tons of leaves, 55 tons of twigs, 364 tons of branches, creepers, and stems of small trees, 210 tons of trunks of average diameter, 266 tons of large boles; which is a total of 964 tons.[5] But could the tropical cultivator do otherwise than he does? The

[1] On the subject of these bush-fires here and farther on, see G. Kuhnholz-Lordat: *La terre incendiée, essai d'agronomie comparée*, Nîmes, 1938.

[2] The Amerindians in the Amazon basin used to burn the trunks little by little so as not to use their wretched stone axes more than necessary. Hence, the arrival of iron implements with the Europeans caused a considerable technical revolution. 'A very few strokes of the steel axe were enough to modify the conditions of labour, to increase the area felled, and double and even treble the harvests.' Hence, after the discovery of America there was among the Indians a thirst for iron as great as that felt by Europeans for gold. Iron gave an assurance of superiority over one's enemies. (A. Métraux: 'Le caractère de la conquête jésuitique' in *Acta Americana*, Jan.–March 1943, pp. 69–82.)

[3] A. I. Richards: *Land, Labour, and Diet in Rhodesia*, Oxford, 1939, p. 288.

[4] See *Agriculture et élevage au Congo belge*, Oct. 1936, p. 157.

[5] According to Beirnaert, p. 40 of *op. cit.* above on p. 17, n. 1.

method he employs is quick and gives him the required area in a short time. The unavoidable deficiency in the means of communication in sparsely peopled countries prevents the systematic exploitation of the forest; and the tropical forest is not easily exploited.[1] (See Photos. 10–14.)

Very often the soil is not turned up. There is scarcely any need for it after the fire, since forest soil is naturally friable and, moreover, fire has the fortunate effect of making it more friable still.[2] Besides, it might be dangerous to turn up the soil too much, lest it should become a prey to erosion.[3]

In Brazil the various operations described above are named thus:—

Brocar = to cut down the undergrowth with a bush-knife, or *tercado*; and perhaps to place the bush on the ground in a layer called a *facho*.

Derrubar = to fell the big trees with an axe.

Picar = to pile up the trunks in order to burn them.

Acciro = space carefully cleared and weeded round the patch to be burnt. This is to prevent the fire from spreading. In the State of Rio de Janeiro the name *bambe* is given to a forested strip between two patches.

Queimar = to burn.

Encoivarar = to make little heaps of trunks and branches not yet consumed in the *queimada* and to burn them again.

Sowing begins after the first rains. A few seeds are put into a hole made with a stick and filled in with the foot. The Kuoys of northern Cambodia have simplified this task by using a tube which allows them to sow the seed without stooping.[4] As a general rule several kinds of seeds and tubers are planted, since in this way are obtained both a main crop which supplies carbohydrates and subsidiary crops which give the wherewithal for making sauces to accompany the boiled vegetables. The variety of combinations is infinite. For example, it has been observed in yam patches in Northern Nigeria that 99 per cent. of the lots had pumpkins as well, 93 per cent. had maize,

---

[1] See below, pp. 75–7, for details of the forest problem.

[2] Sir A. Howard in *An Agricultural Testament*, Oxford, 1943, p. 32, points out that in western India cultivators use fire to make the soil of their seed-beds friable. At the end of the dry season the earth is too hard to be dug, and yet the seed-beds must be set before the coming of the monsoon. To overcome this difficulty the cultivators pile branches on the space to be used as a seed-bed and burn them. The heat breaks up the lumps and gives the soil a friable texture which makes digging possible.

[3] The introduction of the plough into tropical countries is not necessarily an undisputed blessing. See below, p. 122.

[4] In Urundi the women fill their mouths with beans and, without stooping, spit them with amazing accuracy into holes they dig with their sticks.

92 per cent. groundnuts, 90 per cent. red pepper, 80 per cent. beans, and 24 per cent. cassava.[1] Owing to the mixture of crops the ground is covered over with a thick mantle of cultivated plants, which to some extent protects it from erosion.

Weeding is not generally practised. There were no weeds in the forest, and, if by any chance there were some seeds before the ground was cleared, they were destroyed by the fire. Destructive insects and plant diseases are rare in these isolated clearings in the midst of the forest. But the crops must be protected against the ravages of ruminants and birds. Green corn crops attract wild herbivores, and these are frightened away. The Bembas of Rhodesia keep them off by putting up palings. The flights of birds which dart down on the ears of corn are driven off by shouts or volleys of stones. A network of strings is set up over the crops to enable a watchman perched on a platform to sound clappers to frighten away the birds. Certain ingenious Mois have even invented water-driven devices for making protective noises. The cultivators must often leave their villages and temporarily live near the plantation so as to keep a more effective watch. In these ways the crops are saved, unless they attract the attention of a herd of elephants. Patches of cassava have the advantage of not needing such close supervision, since animals do not eat the leaves or roots of this plant. (See Photo. 15.)

All agricultural work is usually accompanied by a grand display of magic. That of the Banhar Reungaos in the mountains of Annam has been particularly well described.[2] Christians in Brazil are not free from these superstitions, and the *caboclos*[3] invoke St. Andrew to secure a wind favourable to their fires. The fact is that bush-burning is the most ticklish agricultural operation in a very rainy land, for if the trees have not had time to dry, they will not burn; and if the cultivator is too late with his fire, he runs the risk of being caught by the first rains. It has happened in Amazonia that clearings have not been planted through not having been fired in time.

The harvest ends the series of agricultural operations, which, taken by and large, have demanded only very little trouble, the heaviest toil being that of clearing the forest. Estimates of the duration of the work required by the *ladang* are very varied. This diversity is in the nature of things and is increased by the difficulty of observation. For example, the Bembas of Rhodesia do about four months' agricultural work in the year, the day's work lasting about four hours.[4] In Brazil some think that clearing alone (*brocar* and *derrubar*)

---

[1] *An African Survey*, by the Rt. Hon. the Lord Hailey, 1938, p. 888.
[2] Rev. Father Kemlin: 'Rites agraires des Reungao,' in *Bull. de l'École française d'Extrême-Orient*, 1909 and 1910.
[3] Brazilian peasants.
[4] A. I. Richards: *Land, Labour, and Diet in Northern Rhodesia*, p. 397.

takes twenty-five days' work per hectare. In the Belem district the cultivator works about sixty days a year on a hectare of cassava.

The technique of the *ladang* may be complicated by the use of the hoe. In forest clearings hoeing is not indispensable the first year, but on the other hand it is necessary in savana clearings. The fire does not destroy the rhizomes of the giant grasses, and the cultivator has to take them out with his hoe to prevent the grass from stifling the corn crops. Then again the use of the hoe is required to break up the soil when the clearing is cultivated for more than a year. The ridges and heaps of earth in which the tubers and cereals are planted are made with the hoe. Hence, very few tropical cultivators do not use the hoe and have not passed beyond the stage of the digging-stick.[1] The work of hoeing is variously divided between the sexes, and whether the chief burden falls on men or women depends on the tribe.[2] The hoe has been variously improved. The Nupes in Nigeria have two, a big one for making the ridges and heaps, and a little one for weeding and other light work. But throughout the hot, wet regions, with the exception of certain parts of southern Asia, none of the cultivators has progressed beyond the hoe. Either for lack of draught animals or of inventive minds, they have not adopted the use of the plough.[3] Although predominantly European by blood and civilization, the cultivators in vast expanses of Brazil have not yet adopted the plough, but use the *enxada* (hoe).

In 1920 there were only 141,196 ploughs in Brazil, 73,403 of which were in Rio Grande do Sul alone. The State of Ceará had one plough for every 2,030 people working on the land, and the State of Pará one plough for every 5,600. Besides, the digging-stick is still used in the *sertão* of Bananal in the State of São Paulo, and in Peruíbe. It is called *chuço, soquete,* or *estaca de cavar.*

[1] The digging-stick remains the only agricultural implement in certain parts of the Toma district on the lower Ivory Coast, whilst the hoe is used in the neighbouring areas. These are curious instances of the juxtaposition of different levels of civilization which very clearly distinguish the human geography of tropical regions from that of the temperate belt.

[2] Daryll Forde: *Habitat, Economy, and Society*, London, 1939, p. 171, when comparing the methods of the Yorubas of Nigeria with those of the Bolokis of Belgian Congo, has come to some ingenious conclusions. Among the Yorubas, who are a savana tribe, the men break up the soil with their hoes, whilst among the Bolokis the task falls to the women. The difference is explained by the physical conditions of the environments. In the Yoruba country clearing off the vegetation is soon done, whilst the hoeing of the hard earth is heavy labour. On the other hand, in the Boloki country the felling of the trees is the main business, whilst the soft earth in the forest is easily hoed. If among the Yorubas who have settled in the forest belt the men still continue to hoe the soil, this is due to the persistence of a custom formed on the savana. These examples of the direct relation between the physical environment and human activities are to be received with interest, but also with caution.

[3] For the possible ill effects of using the plough, see below, p. 122.

The work of hoeing and weeding is often done communally. Neighbours and relatives assemble and work together, and in Africa south of the Sahara the work is done to the rhythm of drums and songs. The slaves carried the custom to Haiti, where it is known as *coumbite*. Brazilian cultivators practise the *mutirão*, which is not appreciably different.

If the same patch is cultivated several years in succession, tropical cultivators employ a system of rotation on it. Various main crops follow each other, the predominant plant being always attended by a train of secondary crops. For instance, among the Nupes of Nigeria yams, cotton, and groundnuts are always the first rotational crop, whilst sorghum and millet are planted in the second year. Among the Bembas of Rhodesia the following rotation is generally observed: ordinary millet (eleusine), groundnuts, early millet, beans and sweet potatoes grown on heaps of earth, and, lastly, sorghum and potatoes also on mounds. The Tivs of Nigeria plant yams the first year, millet (Pennisetum and sorghum) the second, and sesame the third. The crops planted between these are beans, *voandzu*, various hibisci, water melons, sweet potatoes, and cassava.[1] (See Photos. 16, 17.)

After a varying number of years the patch is abandoned and relapses into forest, or into savana if the area is burnt at the end of every dry season. The promptness with which it is abandoned mainly depends on the exhaustion of the fertility (the *terra acabada* of the Brazilians). In the south of the province of Ilorin in Nigeria a savana patch is used for one year only, whilst a forest patch is cultivated for three years.[2] But other considerations, such as the excessive growth of weeds, may come into play. The Bembas of Rhodesia abandon their patches at the end of five years because, since each family makes a new millet patch every year on the *chitimene* system, it ends by having too many patches for the labour supply to cope with.[3] The essential fact is, however, that unirrigated food crops exhaust the soil very quickly. Not that they take an excessive share of bases and nitrogen for their growth, but the bare soil is ravaged by erosion, leaching, the oxidation promoted by changes of temperature and the alternate penetration of water and oxygen, and by the inadequacy of the deposits of organic matter and the speed with which they are destroyed.

Research has shown[4] in fact that the protection of the humus in

[1] G. W. G. Briggs: 'Soil Deterioration in the Southern District of the Tiv Division, Benue Province,' in *Farm and Forest* (Ibadan), 1941, June, pp. 8–12.
[2] J. W. Costello: 'The Forest Conditions of South Ilorin,' in *Farm and Forest*, 1943, Dec., p. 194.
[3] A. I. Richards, *op. cit.*, p. 314.   [4] *Cp.* Beirnaert, *op. cit.*, p. 28.

the soil requires the maintenance of a certain relation between the nitrogen and carbon. It would therefore be less necessary to give the soil organic nitrogen, in the form of green manure for instance, than to keep in the earth an adequate quantity of woody matter which will decompose slowly and secure a supply of carbon over a long period, thus allowing a considerable amount of nitrogen to be kept. The forest yields this woody matter, but dry food crops do not. Hence, it is not surprising to know that such crops waste more than ten times the mineral substances they consume and that recently cleared land may lose up to nearly 900 lb. of nitrogen per acre every year.[1]

The typical agriculture of hot countries is well adapted to the natural conditions. It requires relatively little labour. Now, owing to the many diseases from which they suffer, the inhabitants of tropical lands are not fit to undertake very sustained heavy toil. On the other hand, this form of agriculture shows a great understanding of the conditions of tropical soils. It uses land enriched by the forest and fertilizes it with the ashes of the burnt vegetation; it restricts the attacks of erosion by turning up the soil very little and by respecting the forest all round the patch cleared, so that the soil removed from the latter may not be washed very far. After one or more years' cultivation the cleared patch is abandoned and relapses into forest for a period which may run to twenty years. As M. Auguste Chevalier has well said, the system is one of fallow recurring at long intervals.[2] Owing to the predominance of the forest cover in space and time, the process of destruction of the cultivable soil proceeds slowly. But the period of fallow under forest must last between twenty-five and thirty years for an adequate amount of organic matter to be deposited on the soil. A more rapid rotation is dangerous.

Various agriculturalists stress the difference which exists in Belgian Congo between the Sudanese and Bantu systems of agriculture, the latter being regarded as the better. In the Bantu system after land has been cleared, it is cultivated for no more than two years; and on abandoning it the cultivator often plants trees on it, thus making an artificial wood, or *nkunku*. In the Sudanese system, on the other hand, as practised in the north of the Equatorial Province the soil is tilled with the hoe as long as a crop can be had from it. In the end the land

---

[1] Beirnaert, *op. cit.*, p. 46.

[2] In rare cases, moreover, the fallow may be used for a crop. The following is a ten to twenty year rotation used in Réunion Island:—sugar cane, cassava, legumes or maize, and vanilla under *filaos*. (A. Kopp: 'La vanille dans l'assolement de la canne à sucre à La Réunion,' in *Revue de Botanique appliquée et d'Agriculture tropicale*, 1932, pp. 32–47).

is so exhausted that the forest has great difficulty in re-establishing itself on it.

So then, the typical agriculture of hot, wet lands is remarkably in harmony with the health and pedological conditions. It takes great pains to respect the natural equilibrium and to interfere as little as possible with the slow, delicate processes by which the soil succeeds in maintaining itself and in keeping a certain degree of fertility in the difficult circumstances imposed by the tropical climate. This agricultural system is perfectly rational and manages year after year to produce the carbohydrates needed for human nourishment. Any other system would be difficult if the aim was to obtain those indispensable commodities from unirrigated food crops and to ensure their production in the future. The system may be called primitive,[1] in no disparaging sense, but only with the meaning that, as soon as man ceases to be a food gatherer and becomes a cultivator, he can do no better than use the techniques described above. Though they are certainly primitive, these techniques are nonetheless skilful, and it would be foolish to despise them. The disasters brought on by agricultural methods which have taken no account of the treasures of wisdom and experience accumulated in the old tropical system are a sufficient proof of the latter's value.[2] It can be improved, but only if the reasons for its processes are fully understood. The universality of the technique and its parallel development in human communities which have followed independent lines of evolution show that it is perfectly adapted to the natural conditions of hot, wet regions. There are few such clear instances of identical response by man to similar environment. Facts concerning man do not easily allow themselves to be reduced to unity; and there are in the tropics other systems of agriculture associated with special conditions in the

[1] The temporary cultivation of denshired land has been known in the temperate belt. The forest growing on poor soil was cleared away, the branches burnt, a crop or two taken, and then the forest resumed possession of the clearing. This was a more careless and less progressive type of agriculture than that practised on land continuously used. The backward character of tropical agriculture might be inferred from this, but the inference would be wrong. To see the matter clearly it is enough to recall that crops of this type were in the temperate belt and grown on poor soil, usually on a steep slope exposed to violent erosion and hence on different soil from that generally used in that belt. But tropical soils are poor and exposed to erosion. As a whole they evince features which are exceptional in the temperate belt and found only in clearings made for temporary use. It is therefore not surprising that the usual tropical technique should be like the exceptional technique of clearings in temperate lands. This technique has disappeared in these countries owing to the improved yield of good land, the waning density of the rural population, and the rise in the standard of living of the country folk. But when these conditions are not realized, *ladangs* persist in the temperate belt; *e.g.* in Korea, where the peasants are not primitive, but poor and very numerous. The same is true of China and Japan.

[2] For examples of poor methods of agriculture, see below, p. 118.

6. Laterite at Panjim north of Nova Goa in India. A hard layer of this rock covers most of the surface of the Goa district. When a little soil remains on the layer, thin low forest may grow; otherwise, there are merely patches of poor grass. The pools caused by recent rain indicate the impermeability of the laterite and the tendency of this rock to form enclosed hollows.

7. A laterite terrace at Gurupá on the Amazon.

8. Lateritic soil in Travancore. A crop of cassava is growing in soil, the greater part of which consists of lateritic pebbles. The plants are raised on little mounds which look like heaps of road metal.

9. A termitary in Katanga near Elisabethville. These ant-hills are often as high as fifteen feet and, as there may be four or five to the acre, they reduce the cultivable area considerably.

physical environment and even more with the progress of civilization;[1] but the type of agriculture just described is by far the most widespread.

This agricultural system which is lightly termed primitive and backward was capable of recovering its vigour whenever a favourable opportunity presented itself, without abandoning its fundamental characteristics which were full of wisdom. Among the chief crops grown by African negroes are maize, cassava, sweet potatoes,[2] and groundnuts. Now, these are American plants and cannot have been introduced before the end of the sixteenth century. The negroes have, therefore, been able to adopt new plants and substitute them for their traditional crops which did not give such a good return.

A definite example will give a better grasp of the characteristic agriculture of the tropics. The Mayan village of Chan Kom[3] in Yucatan (see Fig. 7) has a population of 251 persons on an area of 9½ square miles. The people feed mainly on maize grown on the *milpas, i.e.* on their *ladangs.* The land belonging to the village is reserved for the villagers, and they make their *milpas* where they will. A patch is owned by the man who clears it, so long as it is under cultivation, but reverts to communal ownership when it is fallow, though fruit trees remain the property of whoever planted them. As fruit trees are not planted in the *milpas,* this peculiarity involves no complications, but a combination of circumstances has given rise to a paradoxical situation in Chan Kom. At the time it was first built, the village had no plan, and each man sited his house where he pleased. When the village grew, the villagers wanted to give it a good appearance and drew up a plan with a central *plaza* and streets running at right angles to each other. As the houses were moved, some fruit trees found themselves on land no longer owned by the planters, who, however, remained the owners of the trees and could sell them or pick the fruit.

The Mayan cultivator chooses the site of his *milpa* by the appearance of the soil and vegetation, and the ground must have been fallow for seven years at least. As a *milpa* is generally cultivated for two years, the cultivable land is used during two years in approximately ten. Of course, the land belonging to the village is far from being cultivable everywhere. The total area cultivated in a year

[1] See below, p. 99.
[2] Caution is necessary in accepting the American origin of the sweet potato. The certainty of its presence in Polynesia before the arrival of Europeans presents a delicate problem.
[3] M. Redfield and Villa: *Chan Kom*, Carnegie Institution, Washington, publ. No. 448, 1934. See also some details about Yucatan, above, p. 9.

D

(counting *milpas* used for one year and for two) is 300 acres out of a communal acreage of 6,000, *i.e.* 5 per cent. of the total.

The jungle—there are no real forests in Yucatan—is cut down and burnt when dry. The choice of day for burning is a delicate one, for, if the fire is lit too early, there is risk of the wood being too green; and, if too late, rain may put out the fire. Holes are then dug with a dibble at intervals of a yard in all directions and in them are placed five or six grains of maize, some beans, or pumpkin seeds. The grains of maize are taken from the largest ears of the previous crop, and the little grains at the upper end of the cob are thrown away. Sowing takes place in May and June, and not much attention is paid to the *milpa* until the crop reaches maturity in October or November.

A cultivator usually has two *milpas*, the one made in the current year and one made in the previous year, the latter giving a yield between 25 and 50 per cent. lower than the former. Each family cultivates some five acres on the average every year and harvests about 39 or 40 cwt. of maize. Reckoning the consumption in a family of five at $6\frac{1}{2}$ lb. a day, or 21 cwt. a year, there remains a surplus for seed and for sale. The food situation is not bad, for there is no shortage; but the diet seems ill balanced, being deficient in proteins and especially in animal proteins.

Chan Kom lives on the *milpa* after having sprung from the *milpa*. The Mayas, hungry for good virgin land, often go far from their villages to clear a patch outside the village property, but on Federal Government land, the whole of Yucatan not yet being included in areas belonging to any one village. A man who thus clears a patch may make a permanent home, a *milperío*. If he is successful, relatives join him and make an offshoot hamlet, a *rancheria*. A new village, or *pueblo*, comes into being when the connexion with the present village is broken. The parent of Chan Kom was Ebtun, and the original *milperío* dates from 1880.

The causes which gave rise to Chan Kom threaten it with desertion. By 1930 its villagers were clearing *milpas* six and even eighteen miles outside the village lands. Thus, with a density of twenty-six persons to the square mile the land attached to Chan Kom no longer suffices for the needs of the population. If numbers continue to grow, if new *pueblos* go on being formed, Federal land will end by becoming a patchwork of contiguous village properties. What will then be done by cultivators who are eager to make new *milpas* outside their own village boundaries?[1]

---

[1] This need for fresh land has certainly played a part in the former history of the Mayas. See below, pp. 49–50.

CHAPTER 5

CONSEQUENCES OF THE CHARACTERISTIC AGRICULTURE OF THE TROPICS

THE agricultural system most widespread in hot, wet lands has considerable human consequences which give rise to new problems in the exploitation of those regions.

The *ladang* induces a certain kind of land tenure in which the inhabitants of a village are the collective owners of the land related to the village. They may clear any patch they please, but they lose the enjoyment of it the moment they cease to cultivate it. Each man fixes the area of his clearing according to the limits of his strength. Among the Bembas of Rhodesia public opinion also counts, for to make too large a clearing would expose a man to appear presumptuous and be accused of witchcraft.[1] In areas in which the density of population is exceptionally high the liberty of choice gives way to exact regulation.[2] As the land attached to a village is collectively owned and as the various village lands are usually contiguous,[3] unclaimed areas are rare. The establishment of a European plantation in an inhabited district must therefore be carried out with great care. It is dangerous to think that a certain piece of land belongs to no one because it seems to be unoccupied; and it would be foolish to imagine that the rights of the natives are respected by merely leaving them the area they are cultivating, for they require a very large expanse of cultivable land over and above the patches they are actually using; and a really cultivable area proportionate to the length of the fallow period must be reserved for them before establishing European plantations. Any other procedure is mere robbery.

The *ladang* system leads to the concentration of population in hamlets and villages, because the dispersal of the people would be pointless, since the cultivator cannot build his house on his land. The site of the village is always being changed within the area associated with it. This may be for religious reasons, but usually occurs when the village has to be moved nearer to its cultivated patches, because they have been chosen too far from the original village site. A change of position is so normal that there are regular rites for it. West

[1] A. I. Richards: *Land, Labour, and Diet in Northern Rhodesia*, 1939, p. 272.
[2] Daryll Forde: 'Land and Labour in a Cross River Village,' *Geog. Journal*, July 1937, pp. 24–51.
[3] It has been seen above, however, that there are gaps between the village lands in Yucatan. Among the Kundu in the equatorial forest in Belgian Congo there are strips of 'no man's land,' called *ndelo*, separating village lands.

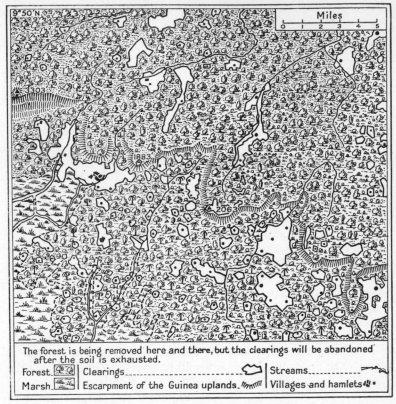

The forest is being removed here and there, but the clearings will be abandoned after the soil is exhausted.

Forest | Clearings .... | Streams ....
Marsh | Escarpment of the Guinea uplands. | Villages and hamlets

FIG. 4. Forest clearings in French Guinea

African cultivators are much attached to their villages and the associated land, but readily accept the idea of a change of site. All that is asked is that the necessary formalities should be observed: *viz.* permission from the supernatural powers and the dead to leave the present site and settle on a new spot.[1] Among the Bembas[2] each family keeps a preferential right to the spot which its house occupied in the deserted village, and the well manured soil yields heavy crops. It may also happen that the site of a village is changed, not because the neighbouring land is exhausted, but because the houses are falling to ruin; it is easier to build new ones on another spot than to try to repair the old ones.[3]

[1] H. Labouret: *Paysans d'Afrique occidentale*, Paris, Gallimard, 1941, pp. 50–3.
[2] A. I. Richards, *op. cit.*, p. 272.
[3] Such a case is described by S. White in 'Notes on Mixed Farming as Practised by some Shuwa Arabs in Parts of Dikwa Emirate' in *Farm and Forest*, June 1941, pp. 24–5.

It must not be thought, however, that concentration of the rural population always takes place in a country where the system of *ray* or *milpa* is in force. Among the Mayas of Guatemala, who are cultivators using the *milpa* system, the population in certain districts is wholly concentrated in villages, whilst in other districts it is altogether dispersed. Thus, Nahualá, with a population of 16,000, has no other buildings in its life-centre than the church, a school, and the town hall. Nothing in the physical environment seems to explain the difference.[1]

The low density of population in hot, wet lands is due in great measure to the poor yields of the *ladang* system, a system which is itself associated with the peculiarities of tropical soils (see Figs. 4, 5, 6). The system cannot feed a dense population, because it uses a small part of the cultivable land (see Fig. 15). A district of four square miles in extent, say, is cultivable in half its area, the other half consisting of over-steep slopes, outcrops of rock, lateritic surfaces, and river beds. On the whole such a proportion of worthless land is not exaggerated in the tropics, but is even rather below the average. If it is agreed that the system of cultivation practised uses the cleared patch for two years and abandons it for ten to the natural vegetation, one-sixth

[1] G. and M. MacCutchen MacBride in *Geog. Review*, 1942, pp. 252–68.

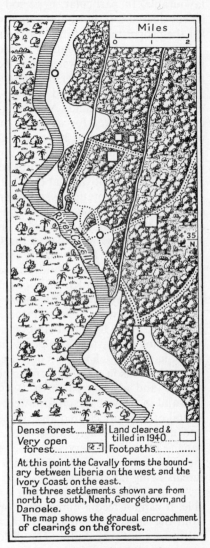

At this point the Cavally forms the boundary between Liberia on the west and the Ivory Coast on the east.
The three settlements shown are from north to south, Noah, Georgetown, and Danoeke.
The map shows the gradual encroachment of clearings on the forest.

FIG. 5. Forest clearings in the lower Cavally River valley

(After G. H. H. Tate, 'The Lower Cavally River,' in *Geog. Review*, 1942)

of the cultivable land will be tilled every year, which is 8 per cent. of the total area, or eight acres in every hundred. A high rural density cannot be supported by so small a proportion of the land. But the figures used in the theoretical calculation above are rather favourable. In particular, a period of fallow lasting ten years may be considered too short, and some twenty years would be preferable for the proper reconstitution of the soil.

The area needed by a family to produce its food by means of crops grown on the *ladang* system has been measured in Sumatra for a family of about five persons and has been found to amount to 15 acres on fertile land and 50 on poor soil. This takes into account only the cultivable land. Assuming that 50 per cent. of the soil is cultivable, 50 acres for a family of five would correspond to an optimum population of 30 persons to the square mile. The *chitimene* system[1] practised in Rhodesia requires about 200 acres to the family, which means that the density falls to 7·7 persons to the square mile. A Nupe family cultivates about 2·25 acres on the average,[2] but the variety of crops, rotation systems, and periods of fallow in the Nupe country scarcely allows of the establishment of a relation between this area and the country as a whole. The same is true of a definite case among the Ndikis who live in the Cameroons about lat. 4° 30′ N. and long. 10° 30′ E.[3] A family of six consisting of one man, one woman, and four young children uses the following areas of land:— around the hut a garden of about 0·6 acre cultivated twice a year, once in the rainy season with maize and sweet potatoes, and once in the dry season with sweet potatoes, maize, *voandzu*, and gourds; a field of 0·25 acre on the savana cultivated in the dry season only, the crops being yams, taro (*Colocasia antiquorum*), groundnuts, maize, and squash; a patch of 0·15 acre cleared in the forest and cultivated in the dry season only, the crops being taro, green vegetables, and squash; and another patch of 0·4 acre used in the dry season for taro and in the wet season for sweet potatoes and maize. This makes a total of 1·4 acre cleared and, if the areas with two crops are taken into account, 2·4 acres cultivated. The cultivation of tubers and banana trees in the very wet zone requires less extensive areas than the cultivation of cereals in the drier tropical zone, the yields from cereals being far smaller.

As the *ladang* system uses only a small portion of the space available, it cannot feed a numerous population. Furthermore, the yield from the areas cultivated is moderate, as the soil is poor and the cultivators not very skilful. The yield from tropical land has already

---

[1] See above, p. 16.
[2] Nadel: *A Black Byzantium*, p. 207.
[3] Mme. Dugast in *Bull. Soc. Études camerounaises*, 1944, No. 8, pp. 69–74.

been compared with that from temperate soil;[1] and a few special facts will complete the information given before. But much research has still to be done in this field, since accurate details concerning the yields from tropical *ladangs* are very rare. In the district of Segu in French

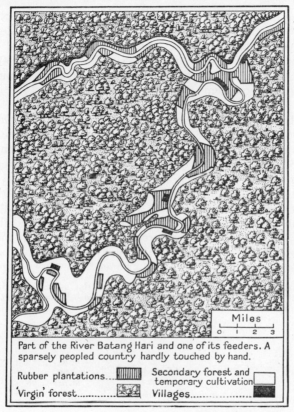

FIG. 6.   Forest clearings in eastern Sumatra

(After Herbert Lehmann, 'Die Bevölkerung der Insel Sumatra,' in *Petermanns G. Mitteilungen*, 1938)

Sudan the following yields have been observed: millet 5 cwt. per acre, maize 4, *fonio* (small millet *Digitaria exilis*) 4, yams 15, sweet potatoes 24, cassava 32, *voandzu* $3\frac{1}{2}$, beans $5\frac{1}{2}$. It has been seen that the yield of maize in Yucatan is $7\frac{1}{2}$ cwt. to the acre.

The production of bananas and tubers modifies the data of the problem. In Uganda[2] bananas form the basis of the diet. On the average in the plantations 61 per cent. of the trees produce fruit

[1] See above, p. 17.
[2] *Agriculture in Uganda*, edit. J. D. Tothill, Oxford, 1940, p. 112.

for baking, 31 per cent. bananas for making beer, 7 per cent. for grilling, and only 0·5 per cent. bananas good for eating raw. The yield is 95 cwt. per acre per annum; yet, in spite of this enormous return, the average plantation cultivated by a family measures only 3·7 acres.

Among the Bulus in the Cameroons[1] the daily consumption of a man who is not underfed is estimated at 5½ lb. of vegetables rich in water, such as bananas, taro, sweet potatoes, yams, and cassava. The satisfaction of these needs requires a cleared patch of 30 perches only, on which about 60 banana trees shelter as many mounds with tubers growing on them.

Cereals, however, form the main crops grown on the *ladangs*, and their poor yield remains the essential feature of the system. As a result, the people of tropical lands are on the whole rather under-nourished and even suffer distressing periods of dearth every year.[2] Irregularities of rainfall[3] aggravate the inadequacy of the yields. In hot, wet regions the lower the total mean precipitation, the more irregular is the rainfall. Districts with a heavy rainfall will always have water enough for the needs of their crops,[4] whilst the badly watered districts may suffer severely from drought.[5] The moment a

[1] *Revue de Botanique appliquée et d'Agriculture tropicale*, 1932, p. 120.
[2] The problems of food supply in the tropics will be examined comprehensively later. See below, p. 65 ff.
[3] See for example E. Biel: 'Die Veränderlichkeit der Jahresumme des Niederschlags auf der Erde' (Festband E. Oberhummer: *Geog. Jahresber. aus Österreich* Vols. 14 and 15, Vienna, 1929.).
[4] Thus:—

Place	Country	Latitude	Mean annual rainfall inches	Driest Year inches	Wettest Year inches	Per cent. of driest to wettest year
Freetown	Sierra Leone	8°29′N.	157	102	206	49
Tamatave	Madagascar	18°9′S.	119	93	158	62
Mangalore	India	12°52′N.	129	89	182	49
Val d'Emeraude	Indo-China	10°38′N.	210	169	246	68
Padang	Sumatra	0°56′S.	174	137	205	66
Accrá	Gold Coast	5°33′N.	27	13	35	29
Diego Suarez	Madagascar	12°10′S.	39	17	57	30
Allahabad	India	25°28′N.	39	19	76	24
Padaran	Indo-China	11°21′N.	30	16	46	34
Kupang	Timor	10°10′S.	57	30	87	34

[5] In hot and moderately rainy lands evaporation annually removes from exposed water surfaces the equivalent of a depth of 80 to 100 inches.

tropical station falls below a mean precipitation of about 60 inches—which is of course a pretty high figure—the irregularity of the rainfall is far greater than in western or central Europe. The ratio of the driest to the wettest year usually falls below 30 per cent., whilst in western and central Europe it remains above 40 per cent. Many tropical countries are thus worse off than temperate lands.

And yet the annual rains are as variable as the rainy season is short, a feature which makes the position of regions with a tropical climate worse than that of regions with an equatorial climate. Lastly, years which were apparently satisfactory in respect of their total rainfall may have had their crops ruined by abnormally dry months. For instance, in western Bengal the famine in 1874 was due to drought in September and October, though the annual total was not deficient.

One great weakness in the *ladang* system is its inability to keep pace with an increase in population. It works satisfactorily so long as a certain balance is maintained between the spontaneous possibilities of Nature and man's needs. If the balance is upset, natural fertility runs the risk of being quickly exhausted. In fact, if the population increases, man either adopts new agricultural methods which give greater yields without harming the soil—as in the case of the flooded ricefield—or else he keeps the *ladang*, but reduces the length of the fallow period. But if the natural vegetation is not given time enough to replace the thick forest covering, the soil will not be able to repair its fertility satisfactorily. Crops will be less good, and, to ensure his food supply, man will be led to extend his clearings still more. The forest replaces itself less and less well as the soil becomes progressively exhausted, and consequently the soil recovers less and less of its fertility during the fallow periods. Besides, the dangers of erosion and lateritization described above[1] become more and more pressing.

The forest can no longer resume possession of certain clearings, which are then occupied by tall grasses springing from rhizomes, the most widespread being *Imperata cylindrica* or *arundinacea* ('alang-alang'). The great danger of these grasses is that they are reduced to the inflammable condition of straw at the end of the dry season and that fires lit to make a clearing are invariably communicated to the grassy areas. A real alliance is formed between the grass and the fire, for the latter may be spread by the grass which, thanks to its rhizomes, is not damaged by the fire. The advantage derived from its rhizomes by *I. cylindrica* is clearly seen from an incident observed in Natal. *Passerina rigida*, another grass, had monopolized the surface

[1] See pp. 20–21.

of some coastal dunes. An invasion by *Imperata* was fatal to *Passerina*, for fires were promoted by the former (which will burn before it is quite dry) and thanks to its underground shoots this grass survived, whilst *Passerina* disappeared. Savanas owe it to fires that they keep possession of the ground. But for fires, in fact, the tree would resume its hold; for the parkland-savana with its fire-resisting trees is in equilibrium in appearance only, the co-existence of trees and grass being contrary to Nature. If there were no more fires, a denser growth of tree would develop.[1] In very rainy countries like the Philippines with a marked dry season, bush-fires have caused vast damage. *Cogonales*, that is, savanas covered with *cogón* (*I. cylindrica*), already cover 40 per cent. of the total area of the group, whereas before man's intervention the islands were certainly clad in a continuous forest mantle.

The damage done by fires is less serious in hot regions with weakly marked dry seasons.[2] All the same, even in a climate as damp as that of Banka in Indonesia, where there is no dry month, bush-fires have a baneful effect. The secondary forest which springs up on the abandoned site of the *ladang* is called *belukar*. If it is left alone for several decades, it ends in a predominant growth of dipterocarps, which are not without economic value. These do not survive repeated fires, however, but give place to a worthless species, *Schima bankana*, whose clusters are easily distinguished by the red colour of their young leaves from the parts of the secondary forest which have not been burnt. If this new association is burnt annually, it may be displaced by savana consisting of *I. cylindrica*.

Of course, fire is far more devastating in districts with a well-marked dry season. In regions of climatic transition burning may compel the forest to retreat.[3] In West Africa oil-palms can be seen outside the forest in complete isolation and accompanied by no young palms. They indicate the former extension of the forest and

---

[1] The question of grasslands and fires will be examined in greater detail below, pp. 56–8, in connexion with stock-rearing in tropical lands. In truth, savana fires are due far more to the interests of the pastoralists than to the burning of patches for agriculture.

[2] See above, pp. 25, 28, on the difficulty experienced in starting fires.

[3] The notes made on this subject by Auguste Chevalier in respect of the forests on the Ivory Coast in *Revue Botanique appliquée et Agriculture tropicale*, 1937, p. 467, are of great interest, for they apply to a district in which the dry season is short enough (three to four months) and the vegetation is rain forest. If a section of the forest were felled without burning, no great harm would ensue, for a secondary forest would soon have replaced the primary. But in the burnt clearings made in the rain-forest grow up 'pan-tropical' grasses which did not occur in the district before the destruction of the forest and which include *Imperata cylindrica, Sorghum guineense, Pennisetum purpureum, Hyparrhenia diplandra, Chasmopodium caudatum*, and *Andropogon tectorum*. These grasses dry up completely at the end of every dry season and burn every year, precluding the regrowth of trees and making the ground more and more favourable to grasses.

the radical changes in environment entailed by its retreat. Young oil-palms were able to grow beneath the forest cover, but can no longer do so in the savana. Besides, many of the palms show a thinning of the trunk just above the roots, a thinning due to fire.[1]

In short, the *ladang* system cannot support a numerous people or maintain the growth of an increasing population. The shortening of the fallow periods, which is an inevitable consequence of the increase in population, involves the ruin of the soil. Among the numerous instances of this occurrence may be mentioned various parts of Southern Nigeria,[2] the Tiv division of central Nigeria,[3] and Sierra Leone.[4] The *ladang* system is at the final analysis an inadequate economic basis on which a high civilization may achieve great political and intellectual attainments.

Nevertheless, the Mayan civilization—whose high standard is proved by the ruins it has left behind—was developed in the tropics. It was of necessity based on a dense population, and its only economic foundation was the *milpa* system. And yet Mayan civilization was perhaps original and did not spring from germs imported from elsewhere. It was therefore very different from the high civilizations of tropical Asia, which are based on agricultural systems, such as the flooded ricefield, suitable for supporting a numerous population and which owe much of their character to influence from outside the tropics.[5] Was Mayan civilization, which has been extinct since the sixteenth century, a denial of the general principles formulated in this book? (See Figs. 7 and 8 and Photo. 18.)

Certainly, a plentiful supply of labour was needed to build the temples whose ruins are scattered through now uninhabited forests on the borders of Mexico and Guatemala. An attempt has been made to calculate the density of population around Uaxactun. For this purpose the sites of houses have been counted within a radius of ten miles around the archæological centre. These traces survive in the

---

[1] On the gradual encroachment on the edges of the forest by bush-fires, see also P. Allouard: 'Pratique de la lutte contre les feux de brousse' in *Bull. écon. de l'Indochine*, 1936, pp. 991–1009.

[2] After one crop the sandy soil of Benin requires thirty years to recover its fertility, and the savanas of Sobo in Benin Province are due to over-cropping. (See *Farm and Forest*, Ibadan, 1941, Dec., p. 119.)

[3] The soil here has become too poor for the growth of *Cassia Siamea*, a tree that is very useful for the rapid restitution of the forest cover. Many other instances might be mentioned; for example, large parts of the district of Abaji in the Konton Karifi division of Kabba Province in Nigeria have been degraded by the Genagena tribe through persistent and too specialized cultivation of gourds; and the population is decreasing owing to the exhaustion of the resources of the district.

[4] See also above, p. 19.

[5] See below, p. 101.

shape of low platforms, for Mayan houses were (and still are) placed on the ground on an artificially raised foundation of earth. If only 25 per cent. of the houses are reckoned as having been occupied

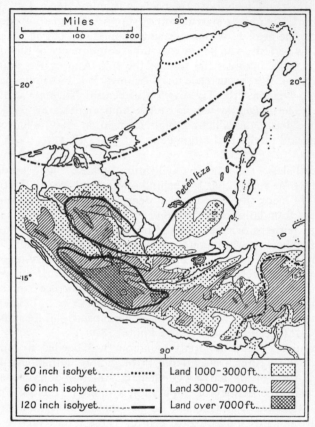

FIG. 7. The Mayan Countries

simultaneously, it may be concluded that 48,000 persons lived within this ten-mile radius. This gives a density of 488 persons to the square mile, a very high figure for agriculture based on the *milpa* system.[1]

The Mayas had reached a high degree of culture, the highest in all pre-Columbian America. Everything points to this: the science and art of building, the beauty of their sculpture, the invention of a form of writing, precise and penetrating astronomical observations, the drawing up of a remarkably accurate calendar and chronology, and, above all, the perfection of a system of notation including the

[1] O. G. Ricketson, Jr., 'Excavations at Uaxactun' in *The Culture of the Maya*, Carnegie Institution, Washington, Supplementary publication No. 6, 1933, p. 3.

discovery of nought and the determination of the value of figures according to their position. In short, a system only slightly inferior to our 'Arabic' notation and having no other equal in the world.[1]

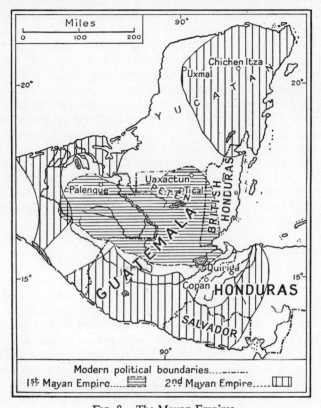

FIG. 8.   The Mayan Empires

(After H. J. Spinden, 'The Population of Ancient America,' in *Geog. Review*, 1928)

Nothing precludes the belief that Mayan civilization was of local origin and came neither from the north nor from the mountains.[2]

[1] S. G. Morley: *The Inscriptions at Copan*, Carnegie Institution, Washington, Publication No. 209, 1920, p. 243; and Morley: *Guide-book to the ruins of Quiriga*, id., Supplementary publication No. 16, 1935, p. 203; and Morley *The Inscriptions of Petén, ibid.*, No. 437, 1938, vols. 1 and 4.

[2] Morley: *Petén*, vol. 4, p. 314. At least nothing precluded such a belief until recently. But now various authors like A. V. Kidder ('Archæological Problems of the Highland Maya' in *The Maya and their Neighbours*, New York and London, 1940, pp. 117–25) think that the mountains of Guatemala may have been either the original home of the Mayan civilizations from which developed the outline of a new civilization that reached its full development in the plain and became the Mayan civilization.

Must the Mayan civilization therefore be considered as an exception, which is all the more remarkable because the country where the first Mayan empire shone in its glory is today one of the least inhabited areas in tropical America? The country is mainly the Guatemaltecan province of Petén and is a typical hot, wet land pitted with marshes, a region of low plains dotted with lakes, the largest of which is Petén Itzá.[1] Most of this little territory is covered with forest, except on certain patches of savana, where the hard red 'clay' may easily be lateritic.[2] The district is almost uninhabited and is only passed through during the tapping season by the *chicleros*, who collect *chicle*[3] destined for the manufacture of American chewing gum. They are wretched folk riddled with fever and tortured by many diseases, not the least distressful of which is *chiclero* ulcer, a leishmaniasis which eats away the ears and the skin of the face and neck. These pitiful people have nothing in common with the strong, ingenious builders and sculptors of Quirigá, Uaxactun, Yaxchilan, and many other towns.[4] Today the administrative centre of the Guatemaltecan province of Petén is Flores, a wretched village with a population of 2,500 persons.

The 'old Mayan empire' made its appearance before the Christian era and prospered until the sixth century A.D. A large population had been able to develop, probably owing to the increased healthiness of the country caused by wholesale removal of the forest. But in the sixth century the old Mayan country became deserted, and the last Mayan city became extinct. The decay of the towns seems to have happened suddenly, for the last date discovered in any of them is given in an inscription which in no way points to decadence, and after this the archæological site offers no further inscriptions. But cities were founded in Yucatan between 120 and 180 miles farther north of the original Mayan area at about the date when the earlier cities disappeared.[5] Though the chief centre of the 'new Mayan empire' was in Yucatan, Mayan settlements were formed farther

---

[1] The mean monthly figures for rainfall and temperature at El Paso Caballo, a point situated to the west of Uaxactun in lat. 17° 23′ N., are as follows:—

	J.	F.	M.	A.	M.	J.	J.	A.	S.	O.	N.	D.	Year
Rainfall	1·8	1·6	1·2	1·9	6·6	9·1	7·7	7·4	11·7	10·7	4·7	3·8	68·2 in.
Temperature	75	78	81	86	86	84	82	83	81	81	78	76	81° F.

(S. G. Morley: *The Inscriptions of Petén*, vol. 4, p. 350.)

[2] S. G. Morley: *Petén*, vol. 1, p. 2. Morley does not use the word 'laterite.'

[3] *Chicle* is the latex of *Achras Zapota L.* and is called *chicozapote* by the natives.

[4] The word 'town' should be understood in a special sense in the Mayan country, for it seems that the Mayas did not in fact build real towns. The buildings which have remained till our times marked rather the life-centres of rural communities. They were meeting-places and not towns, and only priests and officials lived in them permanently.

[5] Morley: *Copan*, p. 459.

north as far as the Isthmus of Tehuantepec and to the south of the old Mayan country in the Guatemala of today, which is now peopled by Mayas. It looks as if the Mayas left their original home in a body and settled to the north and south of it.

The Mayas experienced a brilliant revival in Yucatan shortly after the year 1000. The ruins of Chichen Itzá, Uxmal, and many other places bear witness to this. But Mayan civilization was in an advanced state of decay at the moment of the Spanish conquest, which dealt it its death-blow.[1]

What caused the great migration of the Mayas in the sixth and seventh centuries? If life had followed its normal course in the Petén district, inscriptions would have afforded evidence of it, for there are contemporary inscriptions in the territories newly colonized by the Mayas. The problem has roused the curiosity of scholars, and several solutions have been offered.[2] Did an earthquake devastate the district and drive away the people? But Mayan buildings bear no obvious trace of seismic action, and the dilapidations seen in them are easily explained as the work of vegetation. The same is true of the Khmer buildings, which are situated in identical circumstances. Besides, not one, but several, earthquakes must be imagined, for the abandonment of the old Mayan country took a hundred years. Moreover, this district is not specially afflicted with earthquakes. It is far less so than the mountainous part of Guatemala or Salvador, whose capital, San Salvador, though sixteen times destroyed by earthquakes, has never been abandoned. Man shows no anxiety to leave a district which is liable to earthquakes.

Must a change of climate be imagined? During the existence of the first Mayan empire the climate of the Petén district, we may suppose, was drier and healthier, and consequently the forest was less aggressive. As the climate became damper and hotter and the district more unhealthy, the Mayas presumably abandoned their native land in order to move into more propitious areas.[3] The proof of such a change in climate is said to be found in the growth-rings of Californian trees. During a period contemporary with Mayan splendour, the trees are said to show wide rings which reveal a high rainfall explained as due to the migration southward of the belt of high rainfall in the northwest of the United States. The climatic belts in Mexico are also presumed to have migrated southwards, so that a climate drier and having greater ranges prevailed in the Mayan country. When, on the

[1] Shattuck: *The Peninsula of Yucatan*, Carnegie Institute, Washington, No. 431, 1933, p. 29.
[2] Morley: *Copan*, p. 422.
[3] E. Huntington: *The Climatic Factor as Illustrated in Arid America*, Carnegie Institution, Washington, No. 192, 1914.

other hand, the climatic belts moved back north again, the Mayan country was, we may assume, occupied once more by a damp, hot, climate—hence the flight of the Mayas.[1]

Ought the climatic explanation to continue to be held? No proof of climatic change is found on the spot. The evidence of the rings may perhaps be valid for California,[2] but does it indicate a general displacement southwards of the American climatic belts at the beginning of the Christian era, followed by a retreat northwards in the sixteenth century? Besides, the climatic changes to which such great effects are attributed would not have been considerable. It would have been but a shade of difference, not an upheaval. The climate of Yucatan, whither the Mayas are supposed to have fled to escape the heat and rain of their former country, is also tropical and is merely less humid than that of the Petén district. Yucatan is not a very healthy place, has few people, and seems unable to feed a large population.[3] Lastly, and most important, the Mayas abandoned their original country not only for territory situated farther north, but also moved southwards, as is clearly shown by a map of the position of the second Mayan empire;[4] and the southern settlements are very far from being all situated on high ground. Could a climatic change result in causing southward as well as northward migrations? The fact must not be lost sight of that today about 300,000 Mayas live in the lowlands, whilst 1,500,000 have settled in the mountains. The Mayan area covers the whole of Guatemala, a part of Honduras, Yucatan, and a large portion of the Mexican States of Tabasco and Chiapas.[5]

The purely human explanations are scarcely more convincing than the purely physical ones. The country is supposed to have been ravaged by a Nahua invasion from the north. But nothing proves that the Nahuas invaded Mayan territory,[6] and their advance seems to have been limited to the shores of the Pacific. The final dates of the various cities of the old Mayan empire are spread out over a hundred years, which is a very long time for the conquest of a little country. Would not the cities last abandoned bear witness to the invasion by means of fortifications or epigraphical allusions? But

[1] Karl Sapper is a supporter of the hypothesis of a change in climate; see *Gerlands Beiträge zur Geophysik*, vol. 34, 1931, pp. 333–53.

[2] *The Annual Rings of Trees*, Carnegie Institution, Washington, Supplementary Publications, No. 9, 1937; W. S. Glock: *Principles and Methods of Tree-ring Analysis*, ibid., Publication No. 486, 1937, and critical review by E. Antevs in *Geog. Review*, 1938, pp. 518–20.

[3] See above, p. 8.

[4] Spinden: *Geog. Review*, 1928, p. 651. *Cp.* Fig. 8 above.

[5] G. and M. MacCutchen MacBride: 'Highland Guatemala and its Maya Communities' in *Geog. Review*, 1942, pp. 252–68.

[6] Morley: *Copan*, p. 444.

10. A forest patch being cleared for cultivation at Yangambi in Belgian Congo. At this stage the ground is covered with the bush and trees that have been cut down.

11. The second stage in clearing a forest patch for cultivation. The bush has now been burnt.

12. A forest patch being prepared for planting cassava near Belem in Brazil. In the oven in the foreground the bigger branches are being burnt for charcoal to be sold in Belem.

13. A crop of maize on a patch cleared near Bambesa in Belgian Congo. Trunks and large branches still strew the ground. The oil palms have been purposely left standing, and the other trees which have survived the fire have the bare, straight appearance of forest growths.

nothing of the kind is to be found. Was it civil war? But that this
should lead to the abandonment of the whole country is not evident.
Importance has been attached to an intellectual and political decadence which is manifest in the 'flamboyant' sculpture of the end of the
first Mayan empire. But the technique[1] of the sculpture shows no
decadence; and why, assuming there was decadence, should wholesale migration be the consequence?[2]

There remain the explanations which are based on both physical
and human factors and are associated with the interdependence of
man and his environment. An epidemic might have frightened the
people so much as to make them evacuate the district. Yellow fever
might have been the cause,[3] but on the whole the specialists in
tropical diseases think that yellow fever is of African provenance.[4]
A delay of a hundred years is, moreover, very long for the evacuation
of a country which has suddenly become unhealthy. A sudden increase in malaria might be imagined as a sequel, for example, of
political troubles which might have impaired the cultivation of the
country.[5] But this hypothesis does not square with a delay of a hundred years, and the factors it imagines should have caused a decadence which would have been perceptible in Mayan remains. Besides,
if the explanation of the Mayan migration as caused by epidemic
held good, it would confirm one of the notions which this book will
try to elucidate, namely, that by their unhealthiness tropical lands
are much less favourable than temperate regions to the formation
and perpetuation of numerous human groups and high civilization.

Exhaustion of the soil is probably the best explanation, however.[6]
The pre-Columbian Mayas practised a system of agriculture identical
with that of the Mayas now in Yucatan.[7] Since the former Mayan
empire was densely peopled, the cultivation of maize on the *milpa*

---

[1] *Id., ibid.,* p. 447.

[2] *Id., ibid., id.*

[3] H. J. Spinden, one of the most learned scholars in Mayan matters, finally
falls in with the yellow fever explanation in *Geog. Review,* 1928, p. 649.

[4] See above, p. 10.

[5] The Anuradhapura district in northern Ceylon was abandoned because it had
become fever-ridden. It seems indeed that political troubles started the process
of depopulation by disorganizing the network of irrigation and drainage canals
necessary in this district of swamp rice cultivation. It was on this disorganization
that the malarial complex which caused the depopulation of the country was
based. Technical conditions were not by any means the same in the Maya country, where irrigation was not practised. And if it is true, as some American scholars
think, that pre-Columbian America was free from that worst form of malaria,
the so-called 'tropical fever,' this disease can no longer be regarded as the
explanation.

[6] This hypothesis was first advanced by O. F. Cook in *Vegetation Affected by
Agriculture in Central America,* U.S. Bureau of Plant Industry, bull. 145, Washington, 1909. It is accepted by S. G. Morley in *Copan,* p. 447, and *Petén,* vol. 4,
p. 334.

[7] For this system of agriculture, see above, p. 33.

system without manure, working up the soil, or irrigation necessarily led to excessive shortening of the fallow period and therefore to the utter exhaustion of the land. *Milpas* had to be made at points more and more distant. We have seen above that the Mayas of Chan Kom are already obliged to do this, although they are not very numerous.[1] Still more striking is the case of the Indians now living in San Pedro Carcha in Guatemala. They have turned their district into an un-productive savana and make their *milpas* fifty miles away in the district of Cajabón, whence they carry home the maize on their backs.[2] The former Mayan empire almost inevitably had the same difficulties. The cultivators were obliged to make their *milpas* farther and farther away, but clung to their homes in the old country to which with great trouble they carried part of the harvest. A moment came, however, when it must have seemed impossible to continue the practice. The authorities came to the drastic decision to move the life-centres near to the plantations. Hence, the emigration of the Mayas in all directions, because their *milpas* were situated all round the border of the old centre. To it was also due the sudden end, without any forewarning, which archæology assigns to Mayan towns; and it explains the spacing out of the dates at which the towns were deserted, for the process of exhausting the soil was not completed at the same time everywhere. Lastly, the creation of new towns in Yucatan just when the old ones disappeared becomes intelligible.

The hypothesis is supported by a botanical argument. After a lapse of 400 years the forests of the old Mayan empire are still secondary growths, just as in Cambodia the site of Angkor is covered with secondary forest, though it was abandoned 500 years ago. And yet the insect life in the humus of the present forests in Péten is far from as abundant as in virgin forests, which is a further proof that the forests of this district have been entirely cleared away and have had great difficulty in recovering. Besides, some stretches of laterite are still savana-clad. The clay which has filled various lakes in the old Mayan country must have come from soils eroded through deforestation.[3] May it not be supposed too that exhaustion of the soil contributed greatly to the decadence of the new Mayan empire, a decadence manifest before the Spanish conquest?[4]

---

[1] See above p. 34.

[2] S. G. Morley: *Copan*, p. 454.

[3] A remark of C. Wythe Cooke, the geologist, in *The Culture of the Maya*, quoted by O. G. Ricketson, Jr., in *Excavations at Uaxactun*, Carnegie Institution, Washington, Supplementary Publication No. 6, p. 2. S. G. Morley is of opinion that the filling up is much older than the end of the first Mayan empire. (*Petén*, vol. I, p. 5.)

[4] In *Geog. Review*, 1928, p. 648, Spinden advances interesting arguments against the explanation based on the exhaustion of the soil, holding that there is no proof of the existing savanas of the Petén district ever having been cultivated.

It may therefore be concluded that Mayan civilization is not an exception to the general principles of human geography in the hot, wet lands.

The history of the Mayan people and the explanation of that history would preserve their extraordinary interest if it were proved that their civilization came into being and developed in the Guatemaltecan mountains and was transplanted to the lowlands.[1] The facts would then be much clearer from the geographical point of view, because in that case the brilliant civilization of the Mayas would not present to the world the unique feature of having its origin in a tropical environment. The exception of the Mayas to the rule that hot, wet lands do not spontaneously give rise to high civilizations, but require civilizing influences brought from extra-tropical regions, would no longer cause surprise. The history of their civilization would be like that of Peruvian culture, which beginning likewise in a highland area, spread later to other parts. Mayan history would be that of a civilization which sprang up at a height of about 5,000 feet above sea level and was afterwards moved to the lowlands of the Petén district, probably through progressive adaptations to various altitudes. It would merely have taken the agricultural system in use in the uplands, that is the *milpa* system, without any modification intended to cope with the new circumstances of the environment. But the soil is exhausted more quickly in hot plains than in cool mountains;[2] and when the teeming population of the lowlands had completely used up the soil, it had to abandon the territory of the first Mayan empire.

The history of the Mayan people must have been repeated in other tropical lands, but such striking facts cannot be found elsewhere, because there is no other instance of a splendid civilization, which may have originated in a hot, wet climate and in any event reached its greatest brilliance in such a climate, suddenly moving away and then disappearing almost completely. The case of Anuradhapura

But how could such proof be given? Spinden also observes that all the Mayan towns were abandoned, whether placed on recent alluvium on the flood plain of the Usumacinta or on the thin soil of the Petén district. This objection is a weighty one. But when repeated, the *milpa* is able to ruin the most fertile soil; and we do not know if the areas which were regularly flooded could be cultivated, since the flooding coincided with the maize-growing season. It must be added that no proof has been found that the pre-Columbian Mayas knew the technique of irrigation. It must be admitted that the problem has not yet been completely solved. The Mayas of the first empire were certainly able to practise an intensive system of agriculture without irrigation, but by means of manure and the type of tillage known as *montones*, a technique used in America at the present day.

[1] See above, p. 45, note 2.
[2] Even if the mountains are situated in low latitudes. See above, p. 17.

mentioned above is different, for the civilization to which Anuradhapura belonged was not affected by the fall of that city. The town
of Surame in the Sokoto district in Northern Nigeria lies in ruins in
the middle of a desolate lateritic plain. It may be thought that the
decay of the town, which was perhaps hastened by war and slave
hunting, was caused by excessive cultivation leading to the ruin of
the soil. But this civilization was neither original nor splendid.[1]

[1] J. H. Mackay: 'Perspective in Land Planning' in *Farm and Forest*, Ibadan,
1944, June, I.15.

CHAPTER 6

STOCK-REARING IN HOT, WET LANDS

THE Mayas were not a pastoral people. Their only domestic creatures were turkeys, ducks, dogs, and bees, so they did not bother to make pasture out of the forest. The only purpose for which they destroyed the woods was to clear land for cultivation. The damage done to the forest, and consequently to the fertility of the soil, is far greater if pastoral requirements are added to agricultural needs, as they are in the Sudan, East Africa, Madagascar, India, and post-Columbian America.

Hot, wet lands are not eminently favourable to cattle-rearing (see Fig. 9). First of all, because cattle are exposed to serious diseases there. Trypanosomiasis bars their approach to equatorial Africa, where the only cattle that can survive are small and of low value economically. Besides, the disease, including the terrible East African *nagana*, plays havoc with herds in tropical regions having a well-marked dry season. In Southern Rhodesia the tsetse (*Glossina morsitans*) disappeared after the cattle epidemic in 1896, but from 1918 onwards both insect and disease greatly increased. Energetic measures were necessary to stamp them out by killing all the big wild ruminants and clearing the bush away from strips of country in order to check the tsetse. Many other diseases like cattle plague or pneumonia, may kill the animals. In East Africa attacks of piroplasmosis, heart water, and myiasis are also dreaded. The cattle may be so exhausted by the bites of various flies, such as *Stomoxes*, that stock-rearing would be impossible if the animals were not sheltered during the day in dark stables. This is what used to be done in some parts of Mengo in Uganda (where sleeping sickness was rife) and among the Shuwa Arabs of Bornu in Nigeria. The latter build large circular huts called *tum-tum*, the family sleeping in the middle of the *tum-tum* on a raised platform surrounded by about twenty oxen. The animals stay in this dark shelter from 11 a.m. to evening.[1]

The tropical climate is, moreover, unfavourable to the preservation of pastoral produce: meat, milk, butter, or cheese. But most important of all is the fact that tropical pasture of average quality has no great food value. The flora of tropical grassland is quite different from that of temperate pasture, for it consists almost wholly of

[1] S. White: 'Notes on Mixed Farming as Practised by some Shuwa Arabs in parts of Dikwa Emirate,' in *Farm and Forest*, June 1941, pp. 24–5.

grasses, whilst in temperate pastures it is the leguminous species that are important.[1] How could it be otherwise, since the soil in tropical savanas, being poor in humus, is not favourable to the bacteria indispensable if leguminous species are to flourish? There are some fairly good fodder grasses,[2] but they are rare. Most grasses on tropical savanas quickly become hard and are very poor in phosphorus, which is necessary for the growth of cattle. This by no means surprising deficiency is due to the poverty of tropical soils.[3] Only during the few weeks just before seeding are savana grasses comparatively rich in phosphorus. The most widespread species, found in every continent, are the least nourishing. Altitude makes little difference in the matter.[4]

The poverty of tropical grassland results first of all in the slow growth of the animals. A Malgash ox takes six or seven years to reach its full development. And the beasts need a vast amount of space. It is estimated than an acre of tropical pasture can feed only 48 lb. of live weight, whilst the same area in Europe can feed 480 lb.[5] According to experts in Belgian Congo, it takes at least twice as many acres of grass as there are months in the dry season to feed one full-grown ox in a tropical country. This of course does not take into account areas without pasture.[6] In fact, in Madagascar a zebu uses on the average some fifteen acres of pasture.[7] In the State of São Paulo in a modified tropical climate grassland which is 'natural,' or at least is due to spontaneous growth after the destruction of the trees or shrubs, is of no great value as fodder. Poor pasture, that is, fields of *barba de bode* (a kind of *Aristida*) could only support eight head of cattle per 1,000 acres.[8] Pasture of medium quality in the township of Cunha feeds one beast per *alqueire* (about 5 acres).[9] Good pasture which has been modified by man and artificially planted with *capim colonia, capim jaraguá*, or *capim Kikuyu*, can support just one beast per three acres, provided that the animals are given some maize

[1] B. Havard-Duclos in *Bulletin économique de l'Indochine*, 1940, p. 15.
[2] *E.g.* in Africa *Panicum, Paspalum*, and *Pennisetum*; and in French Indo-China *Digitaria, Paspalum, Setaria*, and *Phalaris*.
[3] See above, p. 16.
[4] Scaetta: 'Les pâturages de haute montagne en Afrique centrale,' in *Bull. Agr. Congo Belge*, 1936, pp. 323–78. See also *Revue de Botanique appliquée et d'Agriculture tropicale*, 1938, p. 783, and 1941, p. 239.
[5] *Cp.* the article by Havard-Duclos referred to above.
[6] It must be remembered that regions with an equatorial climate, and so without a dry season, do not suit cattle in Africa.
[7] In the province of Guanacasta on the Pacific coast of Costa Rica at least ten and often twenty or more acres of pasture are needed for a full-grown ox. See *Geog. Review*, 1943, p. 79.
[8] According to information supplied to the author by Mr. Setzer, an excellent agriculturalist in São Paulo.
[9] Information from Mr. Borges-Schmidt, one of the most competent agriculturalists in São Paulo.

or cotton-seed cake at the end of the dry season in September–November.[1]

So then, hot, wet regions are not naturally adapted to pastoralism. Besides, man has generally taken the natural conditions into account and in these regions as a whole does not confine himself to stock-rearing. His food is mainly vegetable[2] and is perhaps too poor in animal proteins. On the other hand, agriculture depends only to a slight extent on animals either for manure or for work. The *ladang* system makes ploughing unnecessary. If the soil has to be turned over, this is done with the hoe. The plough was unknown, except to the rice cultivators in southern Asia; and its use was spread by Europeans among cultivators of unirrigated food crops. Animals were rarely used for transport. To put it briefly, the agricultural systems of the tropics function as if animals did not exist. There is no appreciable difference between the pre-Columbian *milpa* system, which was established by folk who had neither ox nor horse, nor ass, and the African or Asiatic system of burning out forest clearings. It is as if the system had been perfected by men who knew nothing about stock-rearing and were introduced to it only after having established their agricultural system. In truth, the *ladang* system is in equilibrium and gets on very well without the help of beasts of burden. It must be added that in the tropics most animals are too undernourished to have great strength.

Taken by and large, tropical civilizations tend to be almost wholly agricultural, the reason being that the physical environment is not very favourable to pastoral work. However, there are regions in which, owing to this type of civilization and an inveterate liking for pastoralism, man has developed cattle-rearing. The Sudan and, even more so, East Africa, Madagascar, and India produce cattle. Thus, there is an area to the west of the Indian Ocean in which the same passionate interest in cattle is found underneath differences in race, tongue, religion, and standard of civilization. This area is strikingly different from the Chinese world, which, though not ignorant of the use of beasts of burden, considers them strictly as machines.

Obviously, cattle-rearing is an imported practice in tropical Africa. At the present time the chief pastoral tribes still look like comparatively recent immigrants from the north-east, and people like the Peuhls (Fulas and Fulanis) of West Africa and the various 'Hamitic' tribes of East Africa are quite distinct from the negro cultivators. The practice of stock-rearing has therefore been introduced from the arid regions of north-eastern Africa into the hot, wet parts in which it is not utterly precluded by cattle diseases.

[1] Information from Mr. Setzer. [2] See below, p. 65 ff.

The introduction was on the whole disastrous, for the damage done by pastoralism is incalculable, whilst the economic advantages are insignificant. In fact, the savanas that form the prevailing vegetation-type in the Sudan, East Africa, and Madagascar are mainly due to the need for making grazing grounds.[1] Shepherds are mainly responsible for the fires whose smoke darkens the horizon at the end of the

[1] The problem of the origin of tropical savanas cannot be dealt with here, but on the whole man seems to be the main cause of their existence. Forest is the climax of natural vegetation, even in regions with a very marked dry season. The 'Sahelian' zone on the edge of the Sahara still carries a scrub of thorn-trees. In certain cases the savana is possibly original. See, for instance, Pellegrin: 'La flore du Mayombé d'après les récoltes de M. G. Le Testu,' in *Mémoires Société linnéenne de Normandie*, Caen, 3 fol., 1934–8 (critical review by Auguste Chevalier in *Revue de Botanique appliquée et d'Agriculture tropicale*, 1939, pp. 276–297). See also W. Robyns: 'La forêt équatoriale est-elle discontinue?' (*Journées d'agronomie coloniale*, Louvain, Etab. Ceuterik, 1938, p. 5). The *llanos* of Venezuela, which are immense savanas streaked with gallery-forest, seem to have existed before the arrival of the Spaniards. However, the pre-Columbian Indians did not practise stock-rearing and had no interest in making large pasture lands. Had the Indians had time to destroy the forest by cultivating their *milpas* too often? Mounds, ramparts, watch towers, fragments of beautiful painted pottery have been found, which seem to point to a fairly advanced civilization among the Ashagua, Yagual, and Arichuma Indians who lived on the *llanos*. But the natives were in a state of utter decadence when the Spaniards arrived. (R. E. Crist has studied the influence of the geographical environment on man in 'Le Llanero' in *Revue de Géog. Alpine*, 1935, pp. 97–114.) Today the Venezuelan *llanos* are burnt every year, for the *llaneros* claim that the fire gives them the best pastures and kills the ticks—a belief that remains to be proved. One wonders whether the *llaneros* are not merely subject to an irrational routine. The Kamarakoto Indians, who also live on the *llanos*, ingenuously admit that they like to watch the savana burning. (H. Pittier: 'Consideraciones acerca de la destrucción de los bosques y del incendio de las sabanas' in *Bol. Soc. Venezolana de Ciencias Naturales*, No. 26, vol. 3, 1936, pp. 1–12. G. G. Simpson: 'Los Indios Kamarakotos' in *Revista de Fomento*, Ministerio de Fomento, Venezuela, Nos. 22–5, vol. 3, pp. 201–660; and researches mentioned in *Geog. Review*, 1941, p. 429.) Leo Waibel in 'Place Names as an Aid in the Reconstruction of the Original Vegetation of Cuba' (*Geog. Review*, 1943, pp. 376–96) says that on investigation the word *savana* seems to be of Carib origin. A savana (*sabána*) was a treeless, grassy plain. This certainly points to the natural and original character of some savanas. Waibel is of opinion that before the arrival of the Spaniards 11 per cent. of the surface of Cuba was covered with savana. The problem of the origin of some of the tropical savanas cannot be solved except by exact floristic and pedological researches. But it seems to us that man's action must have been the predominant factor in creating the greater part of the savana areas which are covered with common-place species found throughout the tropics. Thus, it is noticed in East Africa (for example, in the national parks) that the protection of a portion of the savana encourages the growth of trees and makes for the retreat of the grass owing to the stopping of fires. In that way the environment becomes less favourable to the big ruminants and their carnivorous followers, and the fauna is being modified. Ultimately, therefore, East African big game is largely dependent on the fires lit by man. Mr. Leo Waibel has made some penetrating remarks on this problem of the savanas in 'Vegetation and Land Use in the Planalto Central of Brazil' (*Geog. Review*, 1948, pp. 529–54). He concludes that the expression 'savana climate' is wrong. The natural vegetation of the Planalto Central is not savana (though Köppen classifies it as such), but *campo cerrado*, consisting of little twisted trees about a dozen feet high and growing closely together enough to restrict the view, but sufficiently wide apart as a rule to allow a rider to pass.

dry season. The cultivator's clearings[1] and the desire to track down game easily when it has been frightened by fire or to get honey and wax are far less effective causes of the burning. The savana was necessarily made by fire, and afterwards shepherds who wished to feed their hungry beasts at the end of the dry season were forced to burn the tall grass which at that time becomes too hard to be eaten by the animals and is reduced to hard filaments fully deserving of the name 'wire-grass' given to it in South Africa. The fire clears the soil of useless dry straw and at the first fall of rain favours the emission from the rhizomes of young shoots which pierce the sooty soil with pale green tips and give the animals a feast.

Once established in a tropical region, pastoralism is therefore driven logically to repeat its fires every year. The damage done by this is immense and out of proportion to the benefit obtained from the pastoral facilities it procures. It is ludicrous, says Mr. Aubréville, to weigh the advantages of bush-fires against the disadvantages. 'The burning of a house may also have the happy effect of incidentally destroying some nests of termites and bugs.'[2]

In pastoral areas the annual burning of the grass has become a necessary and customary practice. Among the Biroms on the Bauchi plateau in Nigeria the kindling is a ceremony. Hence, it is very difficult to struggle against deeply ingrained customs and the immediate interests of the herdsmen. In East Africa the authorities try to compromise with the evil and do not attempt to suppress it. They recommend early fires to destroy the useless straw and to cause least harm to the trees, for at the beginning of the dry season the trees all have a vegetative rest, whilst at the end of the season they already have buds and little leaves and suffer great damage from fires then. Besides, it has been said that the complete suppression of fires would be imprudent, because if after three or four years' respite fires were to break out anew, the effects would be disastrous owing to the great quantity of combustible matter which would have collected. But the system of early burning finally ends in setting up a shrub vegetation and consequently in diminishing the danger of fire by reducing the area covered by grass. Will the fanatical pastoralists of East Africa accept such a change?

Will the process of soil-exhaustion, which is going on in tropical savanas, be allowed to continue? Burning progressively ruins the soil, and there is a succession of grasses each less exacting, but also less nourishing. In the Teso district of Uganda the first grass to

[1] See above, p. 26 and p. 41, for clearing by fire and complementary views about savanas.
[2] P. 76. Bull. Comité Etudes historiques et scientifiques de l'Afrique occidentale française, 1937, p. 24.

appear after a burning is *Imperata cylindrica*. It is cropped by the cattle until it grows to about a foot high and blooms, after which it becomes too hard. The grasses which grow up a little later are eaten when young, but at the end of a few weeks the cattle avoid some of them like *Trichopteryx*, *Sporobolus*, and *Urochloa*. When the rains come on, *Digitaria*, *Chloris*, and *Eragrostis* appear, but the cattle eat only *Eragrostis superba* and *E. Chalcantha*. On account of the unfortunate selection practised by the cattle and the progressive impoverishment of the soil owing to burning, the savana is gradually changed to bare soil dotted at intervals with tufts of *Sporobolus pyramidalis*. In the Teso district this vegetation-type seems to be the final state of the savana.[1] (See Photos. 19–24, pp. 72–3.)

The evolution is hastened by the tendency among tropical pastoralists to keep more cattle than the natural savanas allow, for the herdsmen take a pride in a large number of animals and care little about the return they get from the herds. Over-stocking brings on the usual consequences, *viz.* exhaustion of the grass and erosion of the soil. The first marks of erosion occur at the drinking pools, where the banks are worn by the feet of too many animals.[2] The activities of certain termites may hasten the evolution. Termites of the genus *Hodotermes* pick green blades of grass in the savanas and may succeed in completely denuding the ground around the termitaries. In consequence of this, violent erosion occurs at the very next rain.

When the land is protected from the abuse of overstocking, the state of the vegetation rapidly improves. For instance, between Timbuktu and Kabara the military authorities have since the conquest reserved an area of 10,000 or 12,000 acres to feed the herds intended for supplying the troops. Wandering tribes are excluded from the area. In about sixty years a 'Sahelian' forest has grown up, with trees 25 feet high. Though less vigorous, the protective measures taken in Gundam in the bend of the Niger have given good results.[3] But could such measures be extended to vast expanses without touching the immediate interests of the pastoralists?

In East Africa 'Hamitic' tribes from the north are much given to cattle-rearing and have communicated their enthusiasm for pastoralism to many Bantu tribes (see Fig. 9). In their scale of values stock-

---

[1] See *Agriculture in Uganda*, 1904, p. 504, edited by J. D. Tothill. On exceptionally fertile soil like the black earth of central Uganda this evolution does not occur or else it takes place very slowly, and the mantle of tall grass (Elephant grass, *Pennisetum purpureum*) is permanent.

[2] For the damage done by overstocking in India, see above p. 19, n. 1.

[3] The facts seem to prove that the impoverishment of the vegetation observed on the northern borders of the Sudan is not due to present desiccation of the climate or the advance of the Sahara, but to bad treatment of the pastures and the damage done by fires.

rearing is a noble pursuit, and a man's dignity is largely measured by the number of oxen he has.[1] Certainly, the animals give meat, milk, and even blood drawn off by skilful bleeding; but the herd is not only useful: it is held in honour. Usually, milking is forbidden to women and reserved to men. Among the proud Batusi in Urundi the men alone have the privilege of milking.[2] They perform the task with great attention to cleanliness, for as a preliminary they carefully wash with fresh urine from the cow the wooden vessel in which the milk is to be caught. Yet they show great clumsiness in the operation, thus proving that, though enthusiastic pastoralists, they are not yet very expert at dairying. In fact, several men are needed for the milking: one or two to hold off the calf, one to quieten the cow, another to protect her from insects, and, lastly, one to do the milking. When two Batusi chiefs meet, they greet each other with the words: 'I hope your cattle are well.' Stock-rearing is reserved to the chief tribe, the Batusi, whilst the Bahutu, a conquered tribe, are restricted to agriculture, though some of them may own a cow or two. Generally speaking, the more or less nomadic pastoralists have imposed their rule on the cultivators, and this has contributed no little to the excessive prestige of pastoralism. The same is true of many Peuhls in West Africa. If through poverty a Batusi abandons stock-rearing for agriculture, he loses caste and even ceases to regard himself as a Batusi.

The young Masai warriors in Kenya and Tanganyika live exclusively on meat, milk, and blood. Among the Masai if an adjective is used without its noun, it is understood to refer to a cow. Among the Nilotic Dinka tribe a father gives a bull to his son on the latter's coming of age. The young man becomes fond of the animal and spends hours playing with it and singing songs to it. The death of a bull causes very great grief to its master.

Every head of a family makes a point of honour to add to his herd, if necessary by carrying off beasts from a hostile tribe. Being too numerous, the animals are underfed, ill-cared for, and in wretched condition. The Chaggas, who live on the slopes of Kilimanjaro and keep their cattle indoors, feeding them with hay cut for the purpose, are exceptional; but they are cultivators, not herdsmen. It is not surprising that owing to peaceful conditions the number of cattle was doubled in the native reserves in Kenya between 1920 and 1933.

---

[1] Some parts of East Africa are so high above sea level as to be no longer tropical. So the conditions are favourable to stock-rearing and afford especially interesting opportunities of *transhumance*. Owing to its altitude and the fertility of its soil the crater of Ngorongoro in Tanganyika has pastures that are still green in the dry season and attract to its 60,000 acres some 80,000 head of game and 20,000 Masai cattle. In the rainy season the crater is deserted, and the vegetation can recover. Stock-rearing is not, however, confined to the high tableland, but is also found at low altitudes teeming with *nagana*.

[2] H. L. Shantz: 'Urundi, Territory and People,' in *Geog. Review*, 1922, p. 346.

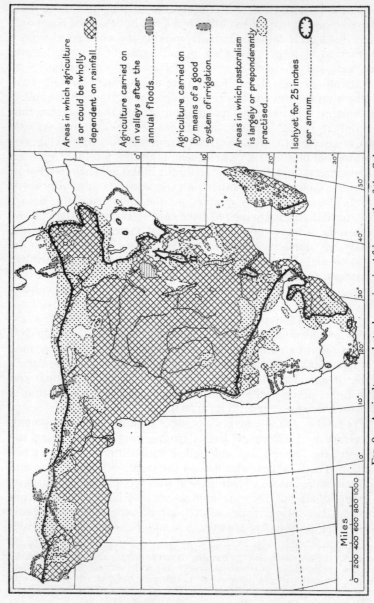

Areas in which agriculture
is or could be wholly
dependent on rainfall....

Agriculture carried on
in valleys after the
annual floods........

Agriculture carried on
by means of a good
system of irrigation........

Areas in which pastoralism
is largely or preponderantly
practised.........

Isohyet for 25 inches
per annum........

Miles
0 200 400 600 800 1000

Fig. 9. Agriculture and stock-rearing in Africa south of the Sahara

(Mainly after F. R. Falkner, 'Die Trockengrenze des Regenfeldbaus in Africa', in *Petermanns G. Mitteilungen*, 1938)

In the latter year the Kamba reserve had 190,000 full-grown cattle and 57,000 calves, whilst its capacity did not exceed 60,000 head. And to the cattle must be added 260,000 goats and 150,000 sheep! So a good deal of the Kamba territory has been ruined, and the inhabitants, who can no longer migrate to other parts, are the victims of severe food-shortage. The situation is no better among the Sukumas south of Mwanza in Tanganyika. It seems clear that ruin of the soil and pastures forced the Jabros to migrate from their original territory, which was situated to the east of Gondokoro in Anglo-Egyptian Sudan, to their present position at Kavirondo to the east of Lake Victoria. The destruction of the soil through over-grazing is becoming a cause for worry in the Teso district of Uganda, where the number of cattle rose from 172,000 in 1921 to 386,000 in 1936.[1]

Cattle diseases, and especially trypanosomiasis (see Fig. 3), seem to be a bar to overstocking. Some people have seen in this a manifestation of Nature's tendency to equilibrium, the rapid multiplication of one form of life being checked by the multiplication of another form. But optimism over the harmonies of Nature seems misplaced, for in fact the fear of losses due to disease is one of the causes of overstocking. As cattle are the only form of wealth among the natives—or the only objects regarded as wealth—pastoralists guard against loss due to disease by keeping herds that are too big. It is difficult to ask them to reduce the number of their animals if at the same time the health of their beasts is not safeguarded. It should be noticed, furthermore, that disease leads to overstocking in another way. In Tanganyika, for example, the pastoralists crowd their cattle into the dry, but healthy parts and avoid the damper, less healthy areas.

It would not be difficult to carry out the improvements which would make pastoralism in East Africa less harmful to the soil and give stock-rearing a greater economic value. The almost insurmountable difficulty today would be to persuade the people to put these improvements into practice. The first reform would be a reduction in the number of beasts. But how could this result be achieved if, as in India, cows have a sacred character or if, as in Ruanda-Urundi, cows continue to play an important part in the social organization? The pastoralists would have to change their outlook and regard their cattle as a purely commercial asset. But should this be achieved, cold calculators might be alarmed at the poverty of tropical pastures and their insignificant yields. Would not our business men regret the absurd period when they considered their beasts not as so many

[1] Many other tropical lands suffer in the same way. An excessive number of goats has ruined the soil over vast areas of the State of Lara in northern Venezuela, where the bedrock now lies bare. (*Geog. Review*, 1944, p. 66.)

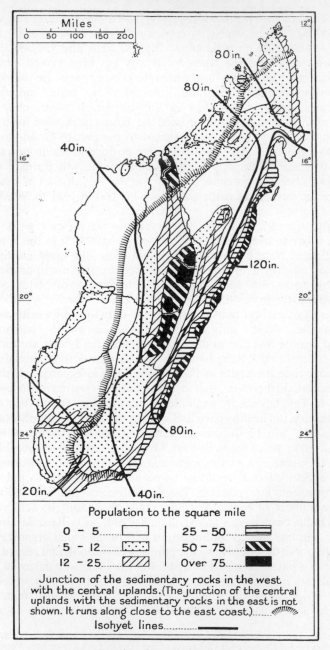

FIG. 10.   Density of population in Madagascar

pounds sterling, but as living beings beloved for their gentle eyes and the colour of their coats?

Madagascar with an area of 228,000 square miles and a population of 4 million (1946), has 6 million head of cattle. The importance of the animals is of long standing and is not due to economic causes, for meat is not a usual element in the diet and milk is not held in great esteem. Oxen were not used for transport, since the Malgash did not know of the wheel, but they were useful for treading down the flooded ricefields before the seedlings were planted out. This enormous number of cattle was indeed scarcely justified by economic reasons. But a large herd won for its owner the consideration of his neighbours, and the Malgash loves his oxen, regarding them as having a kind of soul not unlike that of man. Oxen are the objects of ceremonial washing of the same kind as that given to children and they are spoken of in the family with as much detail and affection as the sons and daughters. The Betsileo dialect has more than 120 names for describing oxen according to their coats. For instance, a *valaloaka* is a black or dark ox with white on all four feet, on the top of its hump, between the forelegs, on the thighs, and in the middle of the tail.[1]

But the animals are scarcely domesticated and are badly cared for. Malgash cows are not easy to milk. It is difficult to detach an animal from the herd, and, when a zebu is to be sold, all its companions must be taken to market with it. The oxen are tired out in immense journeys and are underfed. No trouble is taken to select, nor is there any effort made against the ticks which do great damage to the teats of the cows.

Of little economic value, this stock-rearing has had disastrous effects. Efforts to extend or improve the grazing temporarily have led the herdsmen to adopt the practice of regularly setting bush fires every year, which has ruined the forests and impoverished the savanas. Cultivation on patches cleared by fire and known as *tavy* has contributed to this result, but its ravages are very small compared with those perpetrated by herdsmen.

Before man's intervention the vegetation of Madagascar consisted of forest and bush of a very peculiar composition. Today the original Malgash flora occupies only 27,000 square miles out of the island's 228,000 square miles. The scrub in the south should also be subtracted from the area covered by the original flora. True forest covers scarcely more than 12,000 square miles. This tropical island, which is apparently well watered and has only 18 persons to the square mile

[1] R. P. Dubois: *Monographie des Betsiléo*, Paris, Institut d'ethnologie, 1938, p. 488.

on the average, is already without wood enough for its current needs and has to import timber from the north temperate regions. A town like Tananarive, situated in a wet tropical climate, is without the least source of firewood within a radius of 60 miles.

A small portion of the country, about 16,000 square miles, is still under *savoka*, that is, secondary jungle growing on the *tavy*. But 206,000 square miles are under savana. This savana is perhaps not very old, possibly between 500 and 4,000 years.[1] Thus, in a very short space of time the vegetation-type in Madagascar has been radically changed by fire. The forests on the central mountains were very combustible. Those in the west were more resistant, but were gradually eaten away round the edges. The more fertile the soil the more violent the fires, for on rich earth the thicker grass formed better fuel for the flames. Hence, the forest has persisted only on the poorest soil and in lines along the watercourses.

The grassland is not uniform either in time or space. It varies according to the quality of the soil and the stage reached in evolution. The more advanced the stage, the greater the chance the savana has of being poor. Three states can be defined: first, the savana consists mainly of *Imperata cylindrica*, a tall grass which requires fairly rich soil and disappears as the soil becomes exhausted; this is followed by smaller grasses which are, however, more important from the pastoral point of view, viz. *vero* (*Cymbopogon rufus* and *Andropogon rufus*), *verobe* (*Cymbopogon cymbarius*), *tsimatiloha* (*Andropogon intermedius*), and *danga* (*Heteropogon contortus*); and, lastly, comes the *Aristida* grassland, in which tufts that cattle will not eat are dotted about at intervals, leaving much of the soil bare.

Traditional pastoralism is not very productive in the tropics without the aid of modern science and does a great deal of damage, for it does not conform to Nature's intentions. But clearly, should cattle diseases allow, stock-rearing, when ancillary to agriculture and supplying it with labour and manure, would on the contrary offer great advantages. The keeping of pigs, which utilizes all the waste from the farm, would also be very important.

[1] So Perrier de la Bâthie in *La végétation de Madagascar*, 1921, p. 173. Possibly man has not long existed in Madagascar.

4.

econdary forest in the Mayan
ountains after a vegetable plot
as been abandoned. The forest
as burnt in May, 1945, and the
hotograph was taken in April,
947. The boles are those of Santa
aria trees (*Calophyllum brasili-
se*, var. *rekoi*). Putti palms have
rvived the fire and at this eleva-
on (2,300 feet) a dense growth of
ferns has sprung up.

.

field watchman's platform in
va, showing the volcano Papan-
dayan in the background.

16.
A vegetable plot in a cleared patch in the forest in Jamaica. It is more orderly than usually appears and contains yams, tanyas, bananas, and sweet potatoes.

17.
Native huts and the vegetable gardens nearby. Yams are seen in the foreground and behind are sugarcane, bananas, and other crops.

18.
An imposing Mayan ruin at Chichen Itzá. The grandstand on the pitch where a dangerous ball-game known as *thaxtli* was played.

CHAPTER 7

PROBLEMS OF FOOD-SUPPLY

As tropical man dwells in surroundings which do not greatly encourage the rearing of livestock, his diet is essentially vegetarian. Nothing else could be expected of peoples who know nothing of stock-rearing,[1] but it is surprising to find such a regimen among those who keep livestock.

In spite of their herds, the Betsileo of Madagascar live on rice eked out with cassava, sweet potatoes, maize, spinach, and fruit. Meat seldom forms part of their meals, and milk is unknown. Cockchafer larvæ, caterpillars, grasshoppers, and small fish compose the main part of their animal food. The Fulas (Peuhls) of Futa Jallon, who consume more milk and meat than the average West African negro, feed chiefly on vegetables. Milk, melted butter, and (with all sorts of restrictions) meat figure in Hindu fare; and yet the main proportion of their food calories is derived from cereals and *dhal* (a mixture of chickpeas and beans). Even in the Punjab, where more animal food is eaten than in the rest of India, investigation carried out in Lyallpur has shown that 85 per cent. of food-energy is derived from vegetable matter. The average daily ration of a Hindu rice eater[2] comprises 560 grammes of rice, 30 of peas and beans, 125 of fresh vegetables, 9 grammes of oil and vegetable fats, 14 grammes of fish, meat, and eggs, and a negligible quantity of milk. This ration is deficient in animal proteins and fats, in calcium, and vitamins. It is no exaggeration to say that in the tropics as a whole animal foods do not contribute to the diet more than 4 or 5 per cent. of the total amount of calories.[3]

People living in hot, wet countries display great ingenuity in making use of the resources of the vegetable kingdom. They eat everything that is edible, and so far no reduction in the number of

[1] The Mayas of Yucatan live almost entirely on maize and beans. Meat, mainly game, and eggs form a very small part of their diet, representing only 25 of the 125 pesos' worth of food consumed by an average family in Chan Kom. (Shattuck: *The Peninsula of Yucatan*, Carnegie Institute of Washington, No. 431, 1933, p. 57.)

[2] According to Aykroyd, quoted by Sir L. Rogers and Sir J. W. D. Megaw in *Tropical Medicine*, London, 1944, p. 404.

[3] It is a remarkable fact that in Mexico the Tarascan Indians have borrowed from the Spaniards the practice of ploughing with oxen and that they are nonetheless poor stockmen. Their cattle suffer greatly in the dry season, and the Tarascans of Cherán value their oxen for honorific rather than economic reasons and make little use of beef and milk. (R. L. Beals: *Cherán: a Sierra Tarascan village*, Washington, Smithsonian Institution, 1946.)

plants eaten as food is noticeable among them, though such a reduction is characteristic of modern European civilization. On the Gold Coast there have been counted 114 kinds of edible fruit (which are in fact eaten), 46 kinds of leguminous seeds (groundnuts, beans, etc.), and 47 kinds of green leaves cooked like spinach.

The chief food throughout is a mess of carbohydrates (cereals and various tubers). It is accompanied by sauces which are mainly vegetable and made from leguminous seeds, boiled leaves, fat, oil, flowers, and spices. For instance, in the Mossi district on the Ivory Coast the sauces are prepared with crushed groundnuts, pounded sesame, tomatoes, gumbo (*Abelmoschus esculentus*), hibiscus seeds and leaves, red pepper, leaves and butter from the butter-tree (*Butyrospermum Parkii*), *néré* fruit, baobab seeds and leaves, silk cotton tree leaves (Bombax), and many other ingredients. The quantity consumed in this way is at times considerable. For instance, in the Toma district on the lower Ivory Coast a man eats per annum something like 1,000 lb. of leaves boiled in water or oil. On the other hand, the Brazilian peasant has little interest in greens and lives mainly on maize, cassava, and beans.

The people in tropical lands have arranged their diet almost exclusively of vegetables owing to the fact that their environment does not encourage the keeping of livestock. Nor can the influence of the environment on cultural features be neglected. As a whole, in making use of nature people in the hot, wet belt turn almost exclusively to the vegetable kingdom for their tools, clothes, and dwellings. Like the people in the Far East,[1] they belong to a 'vegetable civilization.' They have evinced the highest degree of ingenuity in getting the best out of certain plants. The innumerable possibilities afforded by the bamboo are well known;[2] and in northern Ceylon the palmyra tree (*Borassus flabellifer*) has no fewer than 801 uses, whilst the oil-palm (*Elæis guineensis*) is quite as valuable to the people of the Guinea coast and is really the basis of daily life.

The fibrous husk of the nut yields oil which is used in the preparation of all kinds of food. The nut is eaten raw. Its oil, though less esteemed, is chiefly used for making cosmetics. After the extraction of the oil, the fibres are carefully kept, dried, and used for kindling fires. The ashes of the male flowers take the place of table salt. When the stalk which bears the bunch is teased out, it makes a good brush for whitewashing walls with lime or kaolin. A fibre used for mending

---

[1] P. Gourou: *L'Utilisation du sol en Indochine française*, Paris, Centre d'études de politique étrangère, 1940, p. 192; P. Gourou: *La terre et l'homme en Extrême-Orient*, Paris, 1940, pp. 20 and 114.
[2] See P. Gourou: *La terre et l'homme en Extrême-Orient*, p. 21.

broken calabashes is taken from the spathe covering the bunches. The leaves are made into roofing, screens to protect young plants from the sun, fish-fences, and baskets for carrying on the back or in the hand. The veins of the leaflets are used for making little fly-whisks which the chiefs carry in their hands. The spines of the fronds serve as rafters. When cut into thin laths, they make rat-traps or snares for birds, and when flattened, they give rough paddles. The juice from the spine is used for healing cuts. The fluff taken off the bases of the leaves catches fire easily and is used as tinder. The central leaf-buds are eaten raw or cooked as palm cabbage. Among the Fangs it is boiled with red pepper to form a remedy for bronchitis. The sap which flows from a hole cut in the central leaf buds is made into palm wine. The roots are chewed as an aphrodisiac. As soon as the tree is felled, the trunk is attacked by the larvæ of a big beetle (*Rhyncho-phorus ferrugineus*), and these 'palm worms' are a popular dainty.

Most investigators into the diet of peoples in the hot, wet belt have found that the diet does not contain the quantity of calories needed by a manual worker. A careful study (which has, however, missed certain details) of the Bembas of Northern Rhodesia has shown that the average ration of a grown man does not exceed 1,706 calories a day, although, according to calculations made by League of Nations experts, the ration of an unemployed man should be 2,400 calories a day, and the miners in Northern Rhodesia are provided with a ration containing 4,313 calories. According to the evidence of Mr. McCulloch,[1] an adult in yam-eating districts should consume every day 40 oz. of yam, between 0·2 and 0·4 oz. of meat, between 1 and 2 pints of whey, and 0·4 oz. of large millet. Now, though the native Tivs in Nigeria eat more or less that quantity of vegetable food, they have neither meat nor milk. How could a wage-earner in Ceylon earning between 40 cents and a rupee a day (1939) feed his family properly, seeing that a man's food (the usual food and not the optimum) costs 15 cents? Similarly, in Barbados the weekly wages of parents, paid on Saturdays, is not enough to ensure the supply of food for the family for the whole week, and many children go hungry to school on Fridays and Saturdays.[2]

The inadequacy of the diet is especially marked at the end of the agricultural year, when stocks are running out. Most tropical peoples go short at that time. Efforts are made to eke out the insufficient rations by collecting on the savana or in the forest seeds of wild grass, tubers, wild fruit, mushrooms, and caterpillars. It is a common

---

[1] *Farm and Forest* (Ibadan), 1944, June, p. 22.
[2] *Nutrition in the Colonial Empire*, H.M. Stationery Office, London, 1939, p. 91.

sight in the African bush to see parties of women in search of these supplementary foods.

Food-shortage is rife even among good cultivators like the Dans and Wobës around Man on the Ivory coast. These people live on the borderline between forest and savana-park, where they attain a density of 20 to 25 persons to the square mile. They cultivate upland rice and have been able to distinguish thirty-seven varieties with different properties; *e.g.* early and late rice. These they sow deliberately according to the qualities of the soil and the calls of the diet, and they have devised five different kinds of rotation which they apply to fields of different qualities. They even attempt commercial agriculture, for they cultivate the kola-nut tree. All the same, they suffer from a considerable shortage in July and the beginning of August and have to eke out their fare by collecting various things, especially the little tubers of a very poisonous wild yam (*Dioscorea latifolia*, var. *sylvestris*), which are not edible until they have been soaked for a long time in water.[1] Food is very short from July to September among the yam-eating Baulës on the savana of the Ivory Coast. The Dogons of Bandiagara in the Niger bend try to protect themselves against famine by building barns big enough to hold two or three crops, but even so they do not always avoid a shortage of food. Though Futa Jallon has the reputation of not being one of the poorest districts and though its population reaches a density of 50 to the square mile, dearth reigns there every year. When their barns are empty, the Fulas fall back on oranges.[2] Among the Bembas of Northern Rhodesia dearth of food occurs from January to March, when the stocks of eleusine are exhausted and nothing remains except gourds, a little maize, and whatever can be collected.

By an unfortunate, but inevitable, coincidence the busiest period in agriculture occurs just when the cultivators are worst off for food. The end of the dry season and the beginning of the wet is in fact the time when the fields must be hoed and the ridges and mounds made, and it is just then that the barns become empty. The work is therefore often badly done because the workers are hungry and disinclined to work.

Being underfed, the people of the tropics focus their attention on the food-supply. The chief topic of conversation in the villages is what has been or will be eaten. The discovery of a nest of caterpillars or a mushroom bed affords a subject for much gossip. They refuse to throw away rotten meat, but eat it, saying: 'We don't eat the smell.' Should a successful hunting trip bring back a good deal of game, the whole village rejoices and celebrates the occasion with dances and songs.

---

[1] H. Labouret in *Ann. de Géog.*, 1937, p. 604.
[2] Ch. Robequain in *Revue de Géog. alpine*, 1937, p. 575.

How is this undernourishment to be explained? The soil is poor, quickly worn out, and gives a low yield. The irregularity of the rainfall has its effect on the crops, and drought sometimes robs even the provident Dogons of their harvests, as happened during the famine of 1914. At times locusts cause catastrophic damage on the borders of arid regions.

The belt of equatorial rains with no marked dry season has as a rule an advantage over regions with a tropical rainfall system. First, the vegetation, both spontaneous and cultivated, benefits from the continuous rains. It has been observed in Belgian Congo that soil poor in chemicals, but enjoying a uniform rainfall system, is equivalent to soil relatively rich in chemicals, but having a dry season lasting four or five months.[1] Besides, the rainfall systems are more irregular when there is a marked dry season. Hence, annual dearths are felt less in equatorial regions. To put it another way, peoples who live on tubers and bananas are less affected by annual dearth than those living on cereals. In an equatorial climate banana trees bear fruit throughout the year, and tubers are harvested at all seasons. Part of the yam or cassava crops can be reaped in advance and the rest left to ripen fully. In Southern Nigeria the peasants cut off the yams near the sprout, for a bit of the tuber with an eye will shoot again and serve as a slip. But the cultivation of tubers is no guarantee against famine, and very many cases of annual dearth have been reported from the equatorial regions. On the other hand, the food-supply may be equally ensured by irrigated ricefields, which have the advantage of producing grain tilled by all the natives in the hot belt and preferred above all tubers.[2]

Tropical diseases are another cause of under-nourishment. Peasants who are weakened by malaria or one of the many parasitic diseases are incapable of hard work. It is a vicious circle, for underfed organs offer weak resistance to disease.

The poverty of the soil, irregular rainfall, and unhealthy climate are powerful factors of under-nourishment. Yet it seems in most cases possible, while still holding to the *ladang* system, to get an assured supply of food either by producing a little more or by acting more prudently in the consumption of the harvest. But here we come to motives of sociology and psychology which have no connexion

---

[1] J. Baeyens, *op. cit.*, p. 22; see above, p. 14, n. 3. The author adds on p. 139 that a rainfall of 55 in. is critical, and less than this causes a drought in the lower Congo region.

[2] Upland rice is equally esteemed. After having exhausted their supply of rice, the Kurankos and Tures of the Ivory Coast eat taro, sweet potato, and cassava from May 1 to August 15. They do not suffer from famine, but are very conscious of the modification in diet, for they prefer rice to tubers.

with the physical environment. To understand them one must never lose sight of the poor state of health—not to say physical dilapidation—of many people in the tropics or the fact that the traditional economy wholly consists of a system of subsistence in which each community has to rely on its own resources.

Custom, habit, and taste are largely responsible for the insufficient production of food. First of all, there is the ancient tradition that, whatever happens, men do not die of hunger because they can always live by collecting until the next harvest. This belief is comforting, but hardly an incentive to work. Natives persist in their preference for cereals, a preference that is probably justified, but should not be carried to the point of neglecting to grow root crops which would save them from hunger. Cassava grows satisfactorily in regions with a long dry season. The good yield which it always gives and its ability to stay in the ground for two years and to have its tubers dug up separately make it a valuable plant which should wholly eliminate the annual food shortage. Contrary to what has too often been stated cassava is not particularly exhausting to the soil. Agriculturalists in Belgian Congo recommend it as the end-crop in the rotation used in native cultivation. If the tubers are left in the ground, they prepare the way nicely for the return of forest growth. It should be added, too, that cassava is making great progress in Belgian Congo. It is spreading eastwards more and more and plays an increasing part in the diet. Formerly unknown in Ruanda-Urundi, it now acts as an important weapon in the struggle against famine, which from time to time used to play havoc with the district.

Slowness in preparing food due to the use of primitive customary methods may be one of the causes of under-nourishment. The most efficient means known to the people in the hot, wet belt for husking grain is the hand pestle and mortar. It is found in every continent, even among people who are in contact with more advanced civilizations; for instance, the Mois in the mountains of Annam still use the hand pestle and mortar, whilst the Annamites in the lowlands have far better implements in the form of a husking-mill and a polishing pestle which is easily worked with the foot.

The preparation of grain by the methods usual among tropical peoples is a long process. Among the Bembas[1] the woman whose task it is to cook husks millet (eleusine) every day. This takes an hour to complete and consists of beating the grain with a pestle, winnowing it, beating it with the pestle a second, though shorter, time, then after another winnowing the grinding of the grain with a stone on a fixed millstone. But every day the cook has also to go and fetch firewood (which takes nearly an hour) and get water (which

[1] A. I. Richards: *Land, Labour, and Diet in Northern Rhodesia*, 1939, p. 91.

sometimes takes an hour when it has to be fetched from a distance). She must also pick in the allotment or the forest the ingredients needed for preparing the sauce which goes with a kind of porridge made of millet, and this may take an hour too. Lastly, water must be boiled to make the porridge, and the sauce must be put to simmer. So the preparation of a meal requires at least three hours. Hence, it is not surprising that there is only one meal a day. Although the Bembas are apt to swallow enormous quantities of millet porridge, the one meal, as may well be imagined, does not give food enough. The mealtime is extremely irregular. It varies between noon and 5 p.m. according to the agricultural activities of the women, and the Bembas, who are quite accustomed to this practice, are not upset either by the irregularity or by the insufficiency of the meals. Sometimes it happens that the housewife is too tired to undertake the three hours' hard work needed to prepare a meal, so she sits down and does nothing. On such occasions the members of her family eat whatsoever comes to hand, an ear of maize or a potato roasted in the ashes. (See Photos. 25–8, pp. 72–3.)

The practice among the Lobis on the Ivory Coast is different, but no better. They live on a mess of sorghum (large millet) and on soup made from fresh baobab leaves and butter from the butter-tree. They do not even use a mortar, and grain has to be crushed whole on the fixed grindstone. This hard task is done by the women, who prepare the sorghum mess every fifth day. Not surprisingly, the mess turns sour on the third day. By the fourth it can only be eaten by being mixed with water. When they go to work in the fields, the Lobis take calabashes containing a little of the sorghum mess mixed with water. That is to be their food during the day's work. The adequacy of such a diet is more than doubtful.

Recent research in the north-east of Belgian Congo[1] has shown that agriculture takes up only about 28 per cent. of the time required by the whole series of operations needed for preparing food, the gathering and disposition of the crop (for example, the storing of the maize) 34 per cent., the preparation (for instance, the pounding of the maize) 38 per cent. The 72 per cent. spent on the process from the gathering to the cooking is certainly a waste of effort.

It should not be too hastily concluded that the annual shortage of food among tropical peoples is due to lack of forethought. Forethought is difficult when every extension of the clearings may hasten the exhaustion of the soil to such a degree as to endanger future supplies. Forethought is difficult when disease saps one's enthusiasm for work; difficult when the social system does not leave the individual

[1] P. de Schlippe: *Bull. agric. Congo Belge*, 1949, pp. 361–402.

the control of his harvest. Why should one reap more grain than one's neighbours since, when they have exhausted their stocks, the more economical man cannot avoid sharing out what remains in his store? Lack of forethought is more clearly seen when the Mois of the mountains of Annam make alcohol from large quantitites of maize which will be needed in time of shortage, or when the negro devotes too much millet to making beer. But alcohol and beer play such a great part in the social life that forethought would appear in these cases to smack of the anti-social.

The food of tropical peoples is not only poor in quality, but is also ill balanced. It is not rich enough in proteins, especially animal proteins, and in fats, vitamins, and mineral elements. In fine, it is without protective elements, and the health of the natives suffers greatly in consequence. The poverty of the food in animal elements is known.[1] Its consequences may be illustrated by a comparison of the vegetarian Kikuyus with the flesh-eating Masai of Kenya, for the latter appear to be better developed physically and to be less susceptible to disease than the former.[2] The very necessary consumption of animal proteins may, moreover, be artificially reduced by absurd taboos.[3] For instance, in Grenada it is believed that milk gives children worms; the Sinhalese consider animals' milk to be the source of many diseases; the New Hebrideans regard it as a revolting form of food; in certain parts of Tanganyika women are forbidden to drink milk; and in some parts of Uganda the same prohibition applies to men. Women are not allowed to eat eggs in some districts in Tanganyika.

No less serious is the lack of vitamins. Together with the lack of calcium, it has been advanced as a cause of the low degree of fertility in Hausa women.[4] It is probably one of the causes of the frequent occurrence of phagedænic ulcers. In certain Nigerian villages a disease of the eyes which sometimes leads to blindness has been cured by means of doses of cod liver oil. Was the disease due to a lack of vitamin A or to the action of poison contained in the cassava which forms the basis of the diet in these villages? It has been recognized that West African negroes purposely eat a great deal of baobab leaf, which is rich in calcium and vitamins. The vitamins are not destroyed if, following native practice, the leaves are dried in the shade before being pounded to powder and stored.

---

[1] See above, p. 65.
[2] Worthington: *Science in Africa*, 1938, p. 572.
[3] *Nutrition in the Colonial Empire*, London, H.M. Stationery Office, 1939, *passim*.
[4] Note 1: Vitamin E is referred to; see Worthington: *op. cit.*, p. 572. Note 2: Villages near which baobabs are common have more fertile women, for baobab leaves, which are used in soups, are rich in vitamins and calcium.

Generally speaking, the food of natives in the hot, wet belt is poor in phosphorus, calcium, iron, iodine, and sodium. There is a longing for salt. This explains many cases of geophagy observed in the tropics. Geophagy pure and simple occurs in North Borneo, Indo-China, and Africa. In the north of the Gold Coast a water-drink is prepared, which is so rich in kaolin as to look like milk, and in Honduras a drink is made by infusing maize in limewater.

The poverty of the food in protective nutriment is most marked at the end of the dry season. At this time the shortage of supplies due to the exhaustion of the stocks of the chief food has not yet really begun—it becomes worse during the early months of the rainy season before the harvest—but fresh wild or cultivated vegetables and fruit are scarce. Just at the time of heavy work in the fields comes a falling-off in the quality of the diet. In anticipation of this difficult period the West African negroes dry the leaves of the baobab and other trees and pound them to powder.

The abundance of protective elements varies with the customs of the peoples. It has been noticed that on rubber plantations in Malaya coolies of different provenance behave differently though placed in exactly the same economic conditions. The Telegus, who are parti-cularly sparing in food, have a very poor diet, whilst the Chinese eat a great deal of soya and pork.

A rise in the standard of living should result in the consumption of food richer in protective nutriment. For all that, an increase in resources should be wisely used. No improvement is achieved if the native buys expensive European tinned food instead of native pro-duce which at the same price would be richer and more plentiful, or if he eats rice husked and polished in a mill and thus runs the risk of developing beri-beri. In Malaya it was noticed that during the greatest slump in the price of rubber in 1930–3 the food situation was better than in times of prosperity. Since the natives were less well off and not so busy on the plantations, they had cultivated many more food plants and had husked their rice at home. Similarly, on the Gold Coast when the price of cacao is high, the production of food locally falls off in quality and quantity.

An increase in population may check the rise in the standard of living and may have unexpected consequences on the diet. In Travancore the main food is rice, which is grown on flooded fields in the lowlands. The growing population has, however, led to the cultivation of cassava on the uplands, and the crop is thus increasingly important in the diet. But the health of the people has suffered because cassava is far less rich than rice in protective elements.[1]

[1] *Nutrition in the Colonial Empire*, p. 54.

Hence, for physical as well as human reasons serious food problems exist in the hot, wet regions. Furthermore, human factors have helped to cause insufficiency in the supply of food and lack of balance in the diet. The number and well-being of peoples in tropical regions will, therefore, depend on the manner in which these food problems are solved. The low yield from labour in these regions is clearly as much bound up with undernourishment as with tropical diseases.

CHAPTER 8

INDUSTRIAL POSSIBILITIES IN HOT, WET LANDS

IT is impossible to deal here with all the industrial problems connected with hot, wet regions. As a whole there is little industry in these countries. Though some people think that the solution of the economic difficulties of densely populated tropical lands is to be found in industrialization, it is only too evident that typical tropical countries—those that are sparsely peopled, comprising some 12 million square miles with a density of 8 or 10 persons to the square mile —should not envisage their industrialization as a matter for immediate attention, but should consider how to improve the use of the land, increase the population, and make the country healthier. The problems they have to face are rural, not industrial.

Countries which are densely peopled, but which, like Java, still remain at the agricultural stage, are obviously by far the most ready for industrialization. The rainy tropical climate does not impose any special conditions on industrialization, and the problems are the same for Java as for north China. Since tropical regions as a whole have little industry, they are clearly backward economically and are looking to Europe and America for their technical progress. What is true of the development of civilization the world over is equally true of economic activity, for hot, wet regions are as backward in the one as in the other.

Man is therefore responsible for the present state of industry in hot, wet regions. It should be noted, however, that the regions do not afford such bright natural prospects as temperate lands in certain spheres of industry, whilst at the same time they do not seem appreciably better endowed in other spheres. Tropical forests are less valuable economically than northern forests, and the hot, wet belt is badly off for coal. The first of these handicaps, connected with climate, is in fact a result of the physical environment, whilst the second is the outcome of geological evolution.

In the tropics there are vast forests with a total area estimated at 6 million square miles,[1] but their value is not in proportion to their size. In 1938 the total world exports of timber[2] amounted to 43

[1] L. and M. Pardé: *Arbres et forêts*, Paris, 1938, pp. 101–3. See also P. W. Richards: *The Tropical Rain Forest*, Cambridge, 1952.

[2] League of Nations, 1939: *Commerce international de certaines matières premières et denrées alimentaires par pays d'origine et de consommation*, pp. 110–30. It would be better to argue from the quantities produced and consumed, but they are far more difficult to obtain.

75

million cubic yards. Of this the tropics contributed only $4\frac{1}{2}$ million, of which 1·8 million came from Asia, 1·4 million from Africa, and 1·2 million from America. All the rest, amounting to 39 million cubic yards, was exported from northern and temperate forests, whose area amounts to 8 million square miles. Tropical forests have not contributed to the world export of wood pulp, which in 1938 amounted to 5,220,000 tons. Many tropical countries import more timber than they export, and they import paper. In short, in 1938 1 square mile of temperate or northern forest exported 2·09 cubic yards of timber and 1,650 lb. of wood pulp, whilst 1 square mile of tropical or equatorial forest exported 0·3 cubic yards of timber and no wood pulp at all.

This state of things is related in some measure to backward economic development, but is due mainly to natural conditions. Tropical and equatorial forests have an economic value inferior to that of temperate forests, and they are more difficult to exploit. This actual situation is therefore very different from the tales commonly told about forests in the hot regions.

The first drawback to these forests is their heterogeneous character. This is in itself an obstacle to exploitation. In Madagascar out of every hundred plants growing side by side in the forest there are always thirty or forty different species, and a count extending over 130 square yards has revealed 239 plants—not all trees—belonging to 102 different species.[1] Under a dead tree young plants of the same species are almost never found; and the life of the forest is a veritable rotation of species. On the Ivory Coast there are at least 500 species of trees belonging to 248 genera and 55 families. On Mt. Makiling, a little volcano in Luzón only some 3,600 feet high, there are more different woody species than in the whole of the United States.[2]

Furthermore, the forests in the hot belt contain a large number of species with wood so soft as to be wholly worthless. They can be used neither for firewood nor for making paper pulp. A census taken on 10 acres of forest in Cochin China recorded 58 different species in 1,080 individual trees with a diameter of more than 4 inches. But 814 were of useless species (*Malvaceæ*, *Sterculiaceæ*, and *Cupuliferæ*). So there were only 266 useful trees, 9 of which had a diameter large enough to make them worth exploitation and belonged to marketable species. It is estimated that in the forests on the Ivory Coast only 1 mahogany tree is found in every 25 acres.

Forests in the hot belt have a very slow rate of growth.[3] This is

---

[1] Perrier de la Bâthie: *La végétation de Madagascar*, 1921, p. 94.
[2] R. L. Pendleton: 'Land Utilisation and Agriculture of Mindanao, Philippine Islands,' *Geog. Review*, 1942, pp. 180–210.
[3] L. and M. Pardé: *Arbres et forêts*, Paris, p. 110.

said to be 0·22 cubic yards per annum per acre in India, where the
rate is exaggerated by the inclusion of the Himalayan forests, which
are not of the tropical type. In Brazil the rate is said to fall to 0·047.
These figures would be improved by the inclusion of more data and
by greater accuracy, and they apply to forests that are uncared for.
But some stands of conifers in the temperate belt grow at a rate of
between 4·2 and 5·3 cubic yards per acre per annum, the average for
France being 1·4 and for Belgium 1·7. It is not surprising therefore
that tropical regions are beginning to be short of timber. For example, Tongking with 13,000 square miles of forest no longer supplies its own needs and has to import timber from Annam.

Contrary to what might be believed at first sight, tropical and
equatorial forests are therefore not easy and inexhaustible sources
of raw materials for industry. The defect can be corrected, but only
at the price of great exertion. It is not enough to make forest reserves,
for though this safeguards the forest, it does not improve it, at least
not in a lapse of time compatible with man's needs. The fact is, useful
species are very slow in getting the better of others, and, if they are
exploited, they tend on the contrary to disappear. The only effective
solution is to fell the trees and plant a homogeneous artificial forest
which can easily be exploited and will replace itself.[1]

Obviously, the industrial development of tropical countries will be
handicapped by the paucity of their resources in coal. Before 1939
the various tropical coalfields produced about 32 million tons a year,[2]
a very small fraction of total world production. Between 28 and 29
million tons came from tropical Asia. This production could be
increased by better exploitation of the coalfields already being worked
and the development of others not yet opened. But the potential is
limited, for countries in the hot belt are to a great extent formed of
old worn plateaus, and crystalline rocks outcrop over vast areas. In
such geological conditions coal is necessarily rare.

Just as lack of coal has been one of the causes of the relative decline
of the countries round the Mediterranean, so it is an obstacle to the
development of tropical lands. Some of the latter are not without
mineral oil, but so far mineral oil has given rise to neither transforming industries nor industrial regions. The equatorial belt has a
respectable supply of 'white coal.' For instance, equatorial Africa is

[1] P. Maurand: 'L'Indochine forestière' in *Bull. écon. de l'Indochine*, 1938,
pp. 801–29. When the wild forest has been cleared away, useful species are
planted at the same time as fast growing trees (*e.g. Cassia siamea*) which hold the
soil together and are used as firewood at the end of a few years. When the latter
species are removed, the useful species are sufficiently developed to anchor the
soil. Of course, the problem is complex, for not every species will live in homogeneous stands.
[2] The Union of South Africa is not included in these figures.

estimated to have a potential of 100 million horse-power. All the same, lack of coal is a drawback in tropical countries as much for power as for chemical industries. India, which is the greatest producer in the tropics with 22,600,000 tons in 1937 and 29,267,000 tons in 1947, is none the less very poorly supplied, considering its area and population. The industrialization of India is being carried out, and among the various schemes published on the subject the best known is the Bombay Plan. But the weakness of all these schemes lies in the fact that the only important coalfield in India is situated far from the sea and from the industrial centres already in existence and bound to develop. The temperate parts of China have an overwhelming superiority in coal, and in face of Chinese industry, which will have as much skill and cheap labour, Indian industry, the most advanced in the tropics, will be able to subsist only under shelter of protective tariffs.

CHAPTER 9

POSSIBLE DEVELOPMENTS IN AGRICULTURE IN THE HOT, WET REGIONS

OUR provisional conclusions from the study of the problems of the development of hot, wet regions are as follows:—The regions are less favourable to man than the temperate belt because they are less healthy and have poorer soil; their inhabitants exist in more precarious conditions; they have adopted a system of cultivation which cannot feed a large population, but neither exhausts the soil nor compromises the future; the introduction of pastoralism does not suit the conditions and has on the whole been unfortunate; and the sparse population, insufficiently and irregularly fed, has been unable to bring a high civilization into being.

The problems of development are closely related to those of population. It is futile and costly to try to make a district healthy when it does not and cannot hold more than a few inhabitants to the square mile. If on the other hand a region can be densely peopled and well utilized, the improvement in its health conditions will be profitable, relatively easy to achieve, and lasting.

It is therefore of the utmost importance to study those hot, wet regions which are exceptionally densely peopled and can provide useful lessons in the development of tropical lands as a whole. Tropical Asia is the best example of human geography marked by dense population, high social and political organization, and the cultivation of swamp rice. A few districts in tropical America and Africa will be studied first here on account of their dense populations and, in some cases, of their agricultural methods, which are more advanced than the *ladang* system.

The West Indies count among the most densely peopled tropical parts of America. The density ranges from 96 persons to the square mile in the Dominican Republic to 1,233 in Barbados, with the intermediate figures of 111 in Cuba, 285 in Jamaica, 306 in Haiti, and 544 in Puerto Rico. This exceptional state of affairs is connected with the advanced economic development of the islands, which have long been engaged in trade and are large-scale sellers of tropical produce, whilst they no longer depend exclusively on their own unirrigated food crops for their supplies.

In Martinique the peasants practise an intensive system of unirrigated horticulture, known as the *trou carré*. They dig a hole with

79

all of its three dimensions between 12 and 20 inches; then in it they place a yam tuber or a cassava slip, filling in the hole with earth and grass. The patches of ground are small and are not what are properly called fields. Yields are good, though calculations of the yield per acre from these tiny areas are rather fantastic (50 to 75 tons per acre for 'Carib cabbages,' tanyas (taro), and yams, and 50 tons for cassava). As the soil is not disturbed apart from the holes, resistance to erosion is good. In short, there we have an interesting response to the needs of a dense population (518 to the square mile) living on fertile soil. But it is at the price of very heavy expenditure of labour and a very modest standard of living.[1] In St. Vincent, however, sheet erosion ravages the arrowroot crops on the hillsides.[2]

Guatemala (see Fig. 8, p. 45) may be taken as typical of the state of things in Central America.[3] In 1934 the population amounted to 2,253,000, i.e 46 persons to the square mile. This relatively high figure is due to the dense population of the central area, which is mountainous and to a great extent situated above the 4,800 foot contour. The province of Sacatepequez, which is almost wholly between the contours for 5,000 and 10,000 feet, had 300 persons to the square mile in 1934. This was the highest density in Guatemala and was really remarkable for a mountainous country. The low-lying districts are far less densely peopled, especially in the north, where in the province of Petén the density falls to 0·54 persons to the square mile and in the province of Izabal to 0·57. Malaria is the chief cause of the difference. Whilst in Sacatepequez, the most densely peopled province, only 12 deaths a year from malaria are recorded for a population of 10,000, the proportion rises to 145 in Petén, the most sparsely peopled province. Hence, central Guatemala owes its dense population to its healthy climate, or, to put it in another way, the fact that it is not quite tropical. But malaria must not be thought to decrease regularly with altitude, for it is virulent up to about the 5,000 foot contour. Larvæ of the dangerous anopheles flourish in elevated lakes like Atitlan and Amatitlan, and malaria is endemic on the shores of Atitlan (5,100 feet), where from time to time acute epidemics are observed. These have probably been due to new stocks of hæmatozoa brought by labourers returning from plantations on the Pacific lowlands. Agriculture is the only means of livelihood of the people in the highlands, for these Mayas do not go in for pastoralism at all. To grow maize they clear slopes so steep that one can

[1] This information is from Monsieur Revert; see E. Revert: *La Martinique, étude géographique*, Paris, 1949.
[2] F. Hardy: 'Soils and Soil Erosion in St. Vincent' in *Trop. Agric.* vol. 16, 1939, pp. 58–65.
[3] G. C. Shattuck: *A Medical Survey of the Republic of Guatemala*, Carnegie Institution, Washington, No. 499, 1938.

19. Grassland in Kenya resulting from overstocking. Note the scattered Kikuyu village.

20. Masai women moving their village across scrub on the Nyeri plains. They belong to a tribe of nomadic cattlemen.

21. An abandoned vegetable plot covered with *Imperata cylindrica* in the Katanga district in Belgian Congo.

22. The Bateke plateau twelve miles north of Brazzaville in French Congo. The plateau top is sandy, and the dry valley has incised meanders and convex sides. The vegetation consists of tufts of grass. This is burnt every year to facilitate the hunting of game. Population density does not exceed five persons to the square mile.

23. Cultivation of the savana near Thysville in Belgian Congo. The top soil has been heaped into little mounds called Mafuka. Nothing grows between the heaps. The grass on the heaps is burnt off and cassava, beans, etc., planted. Note the Leopoldville–Matadi railway in the background

24.
Grassland near Kigali in Ruanda. The animals are protected from the tsetse fly by the elevation of the land. These cattle are valued according to the size and beauty of their horns.

hardly stand on them, and they check soil erosion by heaping up a little pile of earth (*montón*) around the foot of each of the stalks. The piles are placed along the contours and the maize stubble similarly arranged in order to check erosion. Furthermore, erosion is less violent than might be supposed at first sight, for the volcanic soil in Guatemala is very permeable and permits little water to run off on the surface.[1] The soil keeps its fertility owing to its volcanic origin and also to the fact that its chemical decomposition is less rapid because of the elevation.[2]

Yet the unhealthy western district has a density of between 50 and 75 to the square mile, which is much higher than the usual density in the tropics. This is due to the fertility of the volcanic soil (which also influences the high density in the central district) and to the development of plantations on which export crops are cultivated, labour being recruited in the populous highland district near by.[3] The influence of a plantation system is therefore considerable; but such a system cannot develop to any extent unless it has a source of labour-supply.

Altitude also plays an important part in Madagascar (see Fig. 10). The centre of the island is occupied by highlands mostly rising to between 3,000 and 6,000 feet above the sea. On the east of the highlands are narrow alluvial plains and on the west a large basin composed of sedimentary rocks through which broad alluvial valleys run to end in large deltas. The mean density of population (18 persons to the square mile) is normal for a tropical country. But at first sight the distribution of population is surprising,[4] for the most densely peopled parts are the cantons in the central highlands which consist of the districts inhabited by the Betsileo and Merina tribes. Over an area of 20,000 square miles the density is between 50 and 80 persons to the square mile. The alluvial plains on the east are moderately populous with between 25 and 50 persons to the square mile, whilst in certain parts the density rises to 260. Most of the highlands in the centre and west are almost uninhabited, the Kandreho district having the lowest mean in Madagascar, with 0·77 persons to the square mile.

Such a distribution is not explained by the climate, which is nowhere hostile to man. South Madagascar, comprising the Mahafaly and Antandroy districts, is semi-desert, but is not the least densely peopled part of the island, for it contains more people than the Kandreho district, where the annual rainfall is at least 40 inches.

[1] G. and M. MacCutchen MacBride: 'Highland Guatemala and its Maya Communities,' in *Geog. Review*, 1942, pp. 252–68.
[2] See above, p. 17.
[3] See below, p. 109.
[4] Decary and Castel: *Modalités et conséquences des émigrations intérieures récentes des populations malgaches*, Tananarive, Imprimerie officielle, 1941.

Nor is the distribution of population to be explained simply by the soil. Certainly, the most densely peopled cantons on the east coast consist either of lowlands of recent alluvium on which flooded ricefields can be made or else of outcrops of volcanic rocks with plantations on them; but the central highlands as a whole are remarkable for the poverty of their soil, and the alluvial soil in the west is scarcely tilled. Nor is altitude an adequate explanation. In truth, though the most densely peopled belt in Madagascar lies between 4,000 and 6,000 feet above the sea, there are very many parts of the central highlands that are almost uninhabited, and the low plains in the east are well peopled, whilst the lowlands on the west are not.

Is the cause of distribution to be sought in malaria? The matter is not so clear here as in Guatemala. Malaria is indeed rife today in the populous parts of the central highlands as well as on the east coast lowlands and the deserted areas in the central highlands and west. There is reason to think, however, that this was not so until the end of the nineteenth century, before the mixture of peoples which has taken place from that date onwards. Formerly, indeed, the people in the central highlands kept to themselves. Possibly they had become immune to the local stock of hæmatozoa, the virulence of which had perhaps been diminished by the relatively low temperature of the central highlands. It is probable that malaria had been less severe in the highlands for centuries. But it has ravaged them wherever new plasmodium stocks have been introduced, and the Merinas of the central highlands are very susceptible to malaria when they leave their district.

One circumstance in Madagascar, which has no equivalent in Guatemala, must be regarded as very important. The Merinas, who form the most numerous and densest group of people, are less dark in complexion than other Malgashes and seem to be related to the Indonesians. Up to the present they have been superior to other Malgashes in skill, intellectual activity, and political organization. They are different from the other people in the island and are far more apt to make concentrations of population. The cultivation of swamp rice gives a solid foundation for these concentrations.

In short, superior civilization, the flooded ricefield, and, to an ill-defined extent, the action of malaria explain the distribution of population in Madagascar.

The hot, wet parts of Africa[1] south of the Sahara include a few small areas which present an exceptionally high density of population for the tropics. Contrary to a too widespread belief, these blocks of population are not found especially on the healthy highlands. It

[1] See above, p. 10. The Union of South Africa is not included here.

should even be noted that the most important centres of dense population in West Africa do not wholly correspond with the uplands. Other causal factors must therefore be sought.

Central Africa does not vary greatly in population density. The south of French Equatorial Africa is, however, particularly sparsely peopled. The equatorial forest region in the middle of the Congo basin is very sparsely populated, with as a rule about 5 persons to the square mile. Oshwe territory in Belgian Congo has only 2·3 persons to the square mile. On the other hand, the more open country— to the north—the districts of Ubanghi and Welle—and especially to the south (the middle Kwilu, Kasai, and Lulua valleys and Lusambo district) are more densely peopled.[1]

East and West Africa afford a more varied picture and contain a few patches of dense population, but they also include areas which are sparsely peopled according to the norm in tropical lands, and expanses that are empty either because the soil is barren[2] or for historical reasons[3] or on account of drought.[4]

East Africa is essentially a land of savana-parkland carelessly used by cattlemen with peculiar social ideas.[5] In certain districts waterholes are so few that man cannot live in them during the dry season, although the wet season enables crops to be grown. The inhabited areas are small, exceptional, and mainly associated with a more favourable rainfall. The coast strip—what may be called the Swahili country—is a narrow and densely peopled belt. Zanzibar has 241 persons to the square mile, thanks to its clove plantations. In the interior the densely peopled districts lie around Lake Victoria and consist of the Buganda district of Uganda to the north, the Kavirondo district to the east, and the Mwanza and Bukoba districts to the south. To them should be added the Ruanda and Urundi districts to the south-west as well as the region of Lake Kivu in Belgian Congo. Outside this group there are the Chagga district on the south slopes of Kilimanjaro and the Kikuyu district of Kenya. These densely peopled areas are at a high altitude, which gives them a good reliable rainfall. This fosters agriculture, gives greater power of resistance to the forest, and is a somewhat better check on the bush-fires of the

---

[1] According to the map showing density of population in Belgian Congo, published by Robert in 'Considérations suggérées par l'étude du milieu physique Centre-Africain' in *Actualités sociales,* new series, published by the Institut de Sociologie Solvay, Brussels, 1945.

[2] *E.g.* the 'bowals' of French Guinea.

[3] *E.g.* to the south-east of Bobo Diulaso in French West Africa there is a completely empty district 40 miles wide, whose natural conditions are the same as those of the neighbouring districts. War and the slave trade can alone explain the situation.

[4] But then these regions are no longer included in the hot, wet belt.

[5] See above, p. 59.

cattlemen. The healthiness due to altitude plays a secondary part, but it is not negligible. Densely peopled areas in East Africa are, however, seldom high enough to give perfect freedom from disease, and some of the concentrations of population on the shores of Lake Victoria have been ravaged by sleeping sickness and are still threatened with it. In Nyasaland the most densely peopled parts are around Lake Nyasa and the rivers, particularly in the lower valley of the Shire, whilst the uplands are uninhabited. There is a great contrast between the 850 square miles of these lowlands with a mean density of 208 to the square mile and the 20,450 square miles of high plateaus and mountains with a density of less than 10.[1] Malaria disappears only above the 5,000 foot contour.

Densely peopled districts always have agricultural systems that are more intensive than the simple *ladang* and as a rule grow export crops, the profits from which enable the deficit in the home production of food to be made good, if need be. The case of Zanzibar has been mentioned above. The Swahili country is devoted to swamp rice and coconuts. Uganda amasses wealth by selling cotton, and its system of banana cultivation is very skilful, for it avoids erosion and exhaustion of the soil. The system consists of piling on the ground all the green stuff (leaves and stem) that has grown on the area, thus forming a protective cloak over the organic matter. In fact, only the fruit is taken away from the plantation. In the Kikuyu district in Kenya where the system of 'reserves' helps to increase the density of population (see below, p. 129), density reaches 414 persons to the square mile, and the cultivators take precautions against erosion, because the periods of fallow are necessarily shortened. Terraces of a rough kind are formed along contours by piling up weeds taken out of the fields.[2] The density is even higher in the Bunyoro district and in northern Kavirondo. In Tanganyika (see Fig. 3, p. 11) Kitobo in the Bukoba district on the western shores of Lake Victoria has a population of 7,600 on an area little more than 6 square miles in extent, which is a density of 1,230. Ukara Island in the south-east of the same lake is so densely populated that its inhabitants have quite given up the *ladang* system and cultivate the land continuously. Erosion is checked by terraces and by digging little round holes. The soil is manured, thanks to a rational amount of livestock breeding. The animals are kept in byres and fed with cultivated fodder.[3]

---

[1] Dixey in *Geog. Review*, 1928, p. 274.
[2] E. B. Worthington: *Science in Africa*, Oxford, 1938, p. 380.
[3] It naturally occurs to one that isolation and confinement in too narrow a space has driven the Bukara tribe, which lives on Ukara Island, to evolve these improved methods. But has the development really conformed with this reasoning? Besides, is the soil not progressively destroyed by chemical exhaustion and erosion?

But the density of population is so great that many of the young people are obliged to move away to other islands or to the lake shores. They then forget the improved methods of their native island and use the more rudimentary *ladang* system. The southern and eastern slopes of Kilimanjaro carry a population of 150,000 on an area of 200 square miles, or 750 persons to the square mile. The Shaggas have built up a fine system of irrigation for their fields of eleusine and their banana plantations on the fertile volcanic soil. They grow fodder for the beasts which they rear in byres, and they make huge profits from their coffee plantations. In Ruanda-Urundi, where the density of population is 180 to the square mile, soil analysis reveals a satisfactory degree of fertility.[1]

Altitude exercises a favourable influence on the population of East Africa by inducing better conditions of health and, more certainly, by causing a greater rainfall. Conditions are different in West Africa, where the relief is low. Most of the country has a density of less than 25, and vast expanses comprising about half the territory have fewer than 12 persons to the square mile. This of course applies only to districts in which agriculture is possible without irrigation. Standing out clearly against this background are some more populous districts arranged fairly clearly in two discontinuous bands. The northern band runs through the Sudan and includes, from west to east, the San district, Futa Jallon towards Labé, the north-east of the Gold Coast and the Mossi district, the Baulë district on the Ivory Coast, northern Togoland with an extension into the Lama-Kara district in Dahomey, the districts of Sokoto, Katsina, Kano in Northern Nigeria, and also part of Bornu. The other band runs along the Guinea coast rather more continuously from the Senegal to the Cameroons through the Gambia, lower Casamance, the shores of Portuguese Guinea and French Guinea (see Fig. 4, p. 36), the coast of Sierra Leone, the lower Gold Coast, Togoland, and Dahomey, and the Yoruba and Ibo districts in middle Nigeria. The densely peopled parts of these bands are formed of elements ranging between 50 and 130 to the square mile and at times reaching even higher.[2] The greatest densities are attained in Nigeria.

The densest mass of population in Nigeria occurs in the Guinea belt (see Figs. 11 and 12). It is divided into two nuclei separated by a less densely peopled zone which corresponds more or less to the delta of the Niger. On the west in the Yoruba district the density often

[1] H. L. Shantz: 'Urundi, Territory and People,' in *Geog. Review*, 1922, pp. 329–57.
[2] Map of population density of West and Central Africa published on a scale of 1/5M by the Bureau d'études humaines of the Office de la recherche scientifique coloniale, Paris, 1944.

exceeds 260 to the square mile. Although the population is mainly agricultural, it tends to concentrate in large clusters, which is a symptom of fairly advanced development in the social and political spheres. In 1925 there were 84 towns with populations of between 10,000 and 20,000, and 19 beween 20,000 and 50,000. In 1949 the principal towns were Ibadan (pop. 335,000), Ogbomosho (85,000), Iwo (86,000), Abeokuta (57,000), Ede (51,000), Oshogbo (64,000),

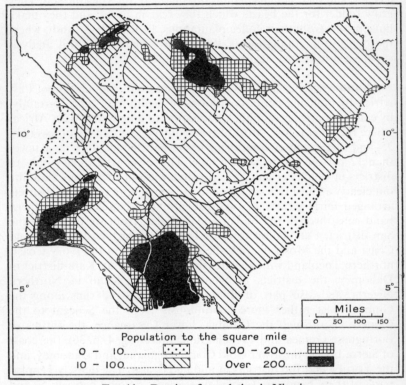

FIG. 11.   Density of population in Nigeria

Oyo (80,000), Ilorin (55,000), and Iseyin (37,000). These clusters are not real towns, but only big villages peopled mainly by countryfolk. The fairly advanced civilization of the Yorubas is evident from their political organization and from their industrial skill, as exemplified by their glass-making, in which they are ahead of other negroes; from their brilliant art as evinced in Benin bronzes; and from their highly developed religion.[1] Mediterranean touches, which have

[1] But the Yorubas were ignorant of writing, and their intellectual development was necessarily limited.

probably come across the eastern Sahara from Egypt, are numerous in their culture. *Cire-perdue* bronze work is an instance of Mediterranean borrowing. Here as elsewhere the higher elements of civilization have not had their origin in a tropical country.

The Niger delta is far less densely peopled. On it backward tribes separated into little groups (Jakars, Sobos, and Ijaws) lead an amphibious life and depend largely on fishing.

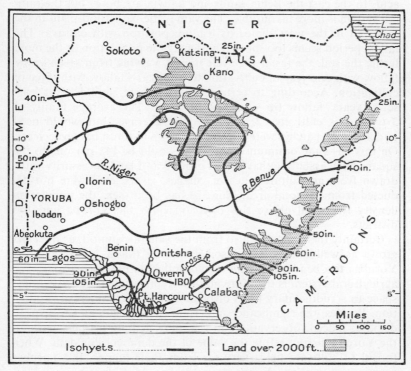

FIG. 12.   Relief and rainfall in Nigeria

The Ibo district to the east of the delta is even more densely peopled than the Yoruba district. The Okigwi division of Owerri province contains 750,000 persons on 1,080 square miles or 700 persons to the square mile. But the Ibos have not made much progress in civilization, having no arts or political organization and only a swarm of tiny clans instead of the skilfully organized regular kingdoms of the Yorubas. The towns, which are small, were created by Europeans and consist of old trading stations on the 'Oil Rivers': Forcados, Calabar, and Bonny, the last having been superseded by Port Harcourt. The great density of the Ibo population is associated with an elaborate use of the soil and long-standing peace, not with an advanced civilization. The same features recur among the Bantu Yakös, who are eastern neighbours of the Ibos.

These high densities are based on the characteristic system of tropical agriculture marked by bush-fires, fallow periods, mixed crops, absence of manure, use of the hoe, and the arrangement of the soil in mounds and ridges. In the west the soil is richer and less acid. In the east the Benin sands and alluvia are poor, but the rainfall system is more favourable. The yam is the basic food-plant in the east, but in the west shares its leading position with cassava. The fallow period seems too short. The denser the population or the more fertile the soil, the faster the cycle moves, varying from seven years' fallow with one year of cultivation to one year's fallow with three of cultivation. According to certain experts[1] there should be at least seven years' fallow for one of cultivation. The average family of 3·6 persons cultivates $2\frac{1}{4}$ acres on the average; but would need 16 acres if the patches were allowed to return to forest for seven years. On this basis the optimum population would be 142 persons to the square mile, assuming that barren ground and land necessarily withdrawn from agriculture (sites of villages, rivers, etc.) were not deducted from the total area. Now, as has been seen, the population density rises well above this figure in both the Yoruba and Ibo districts.

Certainly there is profit also from the sale of palm oil, as the *elæis* grows as well on cultivated soil as in the fallow areas; and the Yorubas too benefit from the cacao and kola-nut plantations. The agricultural system is therefore not utterly invariable, but gives some space to a rudimentary form of plantation and commercial production. Besides, the significance of certain density statistics is open to dispute; indeed, observations in the most densely peopled parts of the Yoruba district refute the value of the demographic data. When forced to cultivate fields very far from their homes, the Yorubas practise two methods. Either some members of the family go and live on the clearings for some weeks during seed-time and harvest, or else the wealthier landowners work their fields by means of serfs who live permanently near the crops. But in either case the produce from these distant fields supports the inhabitants of a locality whose demographic density is thus artificially raised.[2]

Very great density exhausts the soil, however, and threatens it with destruction as soon as signs of over-population appear. Owerri province, which is mainly in the Ibo country, is divided from north to

---

[1] L. Dudley Stamp: 'Land Utilization and soil erosion in Nigeria' in *Geog. Review*, 1938, pp. 32–45; K. M. Buchanan: 'Nigeria' in *Economic Geography*, Oct. 1952.

[2] Daryll Forde: *Habitat, Economy, and Society*, London, 1939, p. 154.

south into five parts:[1] (1) The marshy coast strip (4,130 sq. m.; pop. 139,000) is peopled by Ijaw fisherfolk. (2) A belt some 2,600 square miles in extent (pop. 250,000; density 96) is cultivated to a moderate degree. Secondary forest covers most of the district. Oil-palms are there in plenty, and the people are well-to-do, for there is no shortage of land and a great deal of palm oil is sold. Seasonal immigrants are employed for the heavy farm work and for gathering the nuts. (3) A third belt (1,775 sq. m.; pop. 500,000; density 280) shows signs of being overworked. Many of the young men are forced to emigrate, notably to plantations in Fernando Po.[2] An area of 1,080 square miles is really overcrowded, having a population of 750,000 and a density of 700; and some parts have a population of more than 1,030 to the square mile. Under such demographic pressure the fallow system has become disorganized. The fact is, a piece of land is cultivated so long as it will yield, sub-division of holdings becomes excessive, and food has to be imported to make up the deficit in local production. Imports are paid for partly by the sale of palm oil; but most of the young people emigrate every year and when away from their districts take work as agricultural labourers, craftsmen, or pedlars. The successful continue to maintain their families. The Ibos are not foolishly bound by custom. They would like to improve their agriculture; but this is no easy task, for the soil is poor, tsetse fly prevents the use of cattle, and their land is too greatly subdivided. They would like to be sufficiently educated to be able to get posts in the Government service; but they are too poor to maintain schools above the primary standard, and the pupils from these establishments have had too elementary a training for the purpose. In consequence, there is a growing class of relatively educated unemployed Ibos. The fifth belt (87 sq. m.; pop. 18,000; density 206) displays the unfortunate consequences of excessive cultivation. In much of the area the soil is exhausted and covered with poor grass. Crops are grown only right next to the village, where the soil gets the benefit of chance deposits of organic matter. Though it is not so populous, it is nevertheless poorer than the previous belt.

[1] G. L. Jones: 'The Human Factor in Land Planning' in *Farm and Forest*, Ibadan, 1943, Dec., pp. 161–6.

[2] More detailed information will be found in an article by J. S. Harris in 'Papers on the Economic Aspect of Life among the Ozuitem Ibo' in *Africa*, Jan. 1943, p. 20. The two villages (Ogboko and Njambe) have an area of 6·6 sq. m. and a population of 2,400, *i.e.* a density of 363. Yams are cultivated; and one year's cultivation is followed by five years of fallow. See also an article by C. Daryll Forde: 'Land and Labour in a Cross River Village' in the *Geog. Journal*, 1937, vol 2, pp. 24–51. Lastly, an article by C. Daryll Forde: 'Marriage and the Family among the Yakō in South-Eastern Nigeria,' *London School of Economics and Political Science*, 1941, p. 4. This deals with a Bantu Yakō Umor village, which has a density of 236.

All things considered, the most densely peopled parts of a vast expanse of Africa south of the Sahara are to be found in Southern Nigeria. This great density is due to no special healthiness or high degree of fertility in the soil, though the area is cultivable throughout. Nor is the density explained by superior agricultural skill. A large population can be maintained by reducing the length of the fallow period; but the highest densities must not be of very long standing—in fact, the population has greatly increased during the last few decades— because over-cultivation is a great menace to the future, as is shown by areas already ruined. Great profits are derived from plantations, especially those producing palm oil. Thus at Umor[1] in 1936 every household got an annual return of £2 from its oil-palms. This was a large sum, considering the very small total income of the people. So in these districts the people practise an elementary form of plantation system, that is, an agricultural system particularly adapted to the conditions of the tropical environment, since it maintains the forest cover needed to preserve the soil.[2] A more advanced civilization, quickened of course by Mediterranean influence, explains to some extent the high density among the Yorubas, but in the case of the Ibos does not come into the matter.[3]

From east to west through Northern Nigeria a belt of sparsely peopled territory[4] stretches across the valleys of the Niger and Benue and the Bauchi plateau, which is situated in the interior angle formed by the two rivers. The people dwelling in it are generally backward in civilization.[5] All the same, here and there on the plateaus in the district are found 'primitive' peoples who have improved on the usual agriculture of tropical lands in such a way as to be able to subsist on

[1] See the articles by Daryll Forde quoted in a previous note.

[2] The various writers quoted do not seem interested in the health of the Yoruba, Ibo, or Yakō peoples. Yet it would be very interesting to know what are the repercussions here of the chief endemic tropical diseases, especially malaria, sleeping sickness, and yellow fever. The last two find conditions particularly favourable in this region.

[3] The important work on *The Native Economies of Nigeria* (London, 1946) by C. Daryll Forde and C. Scott must be added to the bibliography. The author came across it under the title of 'Géographie de peuplement en Nigérie méridionale' in the *Bulletin de la Société belge d'études géographiques*, 1947, pp. 58–64.

[4] C. R. Niven: 'Some Nigerian Population Problems' in *Geog. Journal*, vol. 85, 1935, pp. 54–8, with a map showing density of population.

[5] It must be admitted that there is no proper explanation why this middle belt, favoured as it is by the presence of two great navigable rivers, should be less densely populated than the country to north and south. Mediterranean influence, which has been taken into account by E. F. Gautier in *L'Afrique noire occidentale*, Paris, 1935, to explain the density of population and the civilized state of the north and south of Nigeria, would have been especially effective in the valleys of the Niger and Benue. Must one merely suppose that the district has served as a frontier zone between the states to north and south and that it was devastated by war and slave-hunting? Notice in this connexion the very low density in the Nupe district which lies in the Niger valley and which, in spite of its low density, is inhabited by Yorubas.

steep slopes and poor soil. On the Bauchi plateau the Biroms[1] make terraces on the thin layer of poor soil covering the underlying laterite. They use the hoe and they manure their millet fields (*Digitaria exilis*) by emptying all the village waste on them. They have begun to grow potatoes and fertilize their fields by inviting the Fulanis to graze their flocks on them. In Adamawa in British Cameroons the plateaus which extend eastwards towards the central belt of Nigeria are inhabited by a population that is fairly dense in places and employs moderately intensive agricultural methods. Thus, the little tribes of the Wakara, Hidkala, Azgavana, Kuvoko, Matakum, Chikkide, and Glebda[2] pack 52,000 persons into 290 square miles. This great density of 180 persons to the square mile is associated with an intensive, prudent use of poor soil. Part of the district cannot be used, as it is mainly a litter of boulders due to the decomposition of crystalline rocks; and the rest is not very fertile, but is carefully arranged in terraces supported by dry walls. Some of the terraces cover the slopes of hills reaching up to 2,600 feet above the sea. They were constructed long ago, perhaps before the time of the present tribes. As a rule they are not more than 7 or 10 feet wide, and some are so narrow that they take only one row of millet. By the use of manure fallow is nearly eliminated, being reduced to about two years in fifteen. To get manure the peasants rear horned cattle, goats, and sheep, and carefully collect the dung from the sheds in which the animals spend the night. The hoe is used, and there is a satisfactory rotation of crops. Trees are planted for use as firewood and for building, and their leaves are used as fodder.

The methods of cultivation used on the plateaus of Bauchi and Adamawa seem ahead of those usual in hot, wet regions. Unfortunately, they appear to have been developed by tribes that were forced ahead by reasons of security. They fled into rather inaccessible districts of broken relief in order to escape their enemies on the plains, and in the mountains developed methods of intensive exploitation. But these methods have not made them prosperous. If the danger feared by the tribes disappears, they go down to the lowland and there use careless methods, the terraces in the mountains are carried away by erosion, and the slopes are left bare. This is what has happened in Adamawa to the slopes occupied by the Azgavana and Matakums.[3] A similar state of things is seen in Kenya, where the Kambas have left their mountain abode for the lowlands.

[1] Suffil in *Farm and Forest*, Dec. 1943, pp. 179–82.
[2] S. White: 'Agricultural Economy of the Hill Pagans of Dikwa Emirate, Cameroons (British Mandate)' in *Farm and Forest*, Sept. 1944, pp. 130–4.
[3] But on the borders of Adamawa the Bamileke in French Cameroons flourish on their plateaus and create a density amounting to 260 persons to the square mile. M. Sanmarco in *Annales de Géog.*, 1945, p. 224.

The parts of Nigeria lying within the Sudan have a mean density of 41 persons to the square mile, which is very high for Africa south of the Sahara. In the centre near Kano the density exceeds 130 within a considerable radius around the town and 1,340 within a radius of 10 miles. Kano itself has a population of about 100,000.[1] The people of the district are Hausas, a mixture of Hamitic elements with Sudanese negroes. They have a high culture containing features borrowed from the eastern Mediterranean. The Hausas are Muslims and use the Arabic alphabet for writing their own language. Many of them can read and write Arabic. A complex political organization meets the needs of the large population.

Generally, the agricultural system is that of the *ladang*. But the climate is dry, and bush fires are lit every year, so that fertility does not very well recover during the period of fallow when the land returns to forest. The Hausa peasant turns over his soil with the hoe, an easy matter in this sandy area. In this way he removes the rhizomes of big grasses which would compete with his crops, and he digs little hollows—not mounds, as is done in moister regions. The chief plant is sorghum (large millet), but there are many minor ones. Every family (3·3 persons on the average) cultivates about 3 acres a year.[2] So, as the fallow with its woodland growth should continue at least seven years if it is to be profitable, every family needs 24 acres. On this basis the optimum population would be 88 persons to the square mile, if barren land is not deducted from the total area. In the parts of Nigeria lying within the Sudan there are districts which exceed this density. How is this to be explained?

Cultivation is generally careful and is helped by the fairly flat relief. Soil erosion is reduced to a minimum by the crops being planted in holes and a large number of trees being kept to fix the soil with their roots. Though the country around Kano is intensively cultivated, it looks like parkland. Furthermore, the Hausas get a part of their living by keeping livestock; hence, they practise mixed farming. They drink milk and carefully manure their fields. They live symbiotically with the Fulani shepherds and make contracts with them for tending their flocks. In this way the settled folk make some use of the sparsely peopled areas which they do not cultivate, but whose resources contribute to the livelihood of the inhabitants of the densely populated districts. The Hausas have taken up an export crop, the groundnut, which completes their means of earning a living. Taking one year with another, the railway station at Kano

[1] Whittlesey: 'Kano, a Sudanese Metropolis' in *Geog. Review*, 1937, pp. 177–99.
[2] L. Dudley Stamp: 'Land Utilisation and Soil Erosion in Nigeria' in *Geog. Review*, 1938, pp. 32–45.

despatches 150,000 tons of groundnuts to the coast. The groundnut is a leguminous plant which easily finds a place in the cycle of crops.

In the densely populated parts agriculture has assumed a very different character from the usual tropical type. Swamp rice is planted near Sokoto. The countryfolk around Kano go in for real market-gardening, and the soil is often worked all through the year without rest, thanks to the manure brought from the town. Crops are grown in the dry season by means of irrigation. Wells fitted with *shadufs* bring water up from the water table, where there is a good supply owing to the geological structure, for water from the hills to the south flows along the plane of junction of the crystalline strata which tilt very gently down under the mantle of sand.

In fine, moderately favourable local conditions have allowed the development of intensive agricultural methods which ensure the livelihood of a large population. But human factors still predominate. An advanced civilization rich in elements borrowed from the Mediterranean was needed to interpret the natural conditions in a sense favourable to a large population. Besides, the natural conditions are not permanently favourable over sufficiently large areas in the Sudan to enable human systems to last long, and historical developments have had great influence on those systems. According to Y. Urvoy[1] areas of dense population in the Sudan are associated not with agricultural methods, which are nearly the same everywhere, but with historical facts. Large states secure peace and allow of dense populations. In the west the states capable of playing such a part have long since decayed. Ghana was at its zenith about the year 1000, Mali in the thirteenth and fourteenth centuries, and the Sonrai empire in the sixteenth century. On the other hand, the states in the east are recent and still in existence. The Hausas and Mossis did not begin to form huge states till the sixteenth century. It may well be that natural conditions in the hot, wet region were strong factors in bringing about the decline of the former Sudanese empires, whose populations, if numerous, must have excessively used the soil for agriculture and have exhausted it.

The flooded ricefield plays a small part in the economy of West Africa, even in districts in which natural conditions make it possible. This is a mark of backward civilization, for the flooded ricefield offers mankind in the tropics the best chance of a yearly production of a sufficiency of carbohydrates with a minimum of manure,[2] and

---

[1] *Petit atlas démographique du Soudan entre Sénégal et Tchad*, Paris, 1942, p. 14.
[2] See below, p. 100.

without fallow periods or risk of erosion or exhaustion of the soil. The system of rice cultivation in the Niger valley above the delta is very primitive. The fields are flooded by inundations of the river and are not true irrigated ricefields. The young shoots are seldom planted out, though this would prevent loss due to the irregularity of the floods of the river and to greedy fish that like to eat the rice blades.

Rice cultivation is more intensive at certain points in the Guinea zone. The inhabitants of lower Casamance (Diola), of the Bolama Islands, and the lower Scarcie (Temne, Mende in Sierra Leone) have cleared away the mangroves and embanked plots of ground which they have freed from salt by digging the soil deeply with the hoe and leaving it to be leached by rain and river water when the latter is fresh. Replanting is necessary, for when the ricefields are at last flooded with fresh water after the end of the rainy season, it allows largish plants to be set out. These will grow during the rains, whilst direct sowing would put back the date of ripening too far. There are practically no fields lying fallow, and in some places two rice harvests a year are reported.[1]

But this use of the flooded ricefield is strictly localized and is very far from occupying all the space it well could. For instance, in Sierra Leone the increasing population has led to the shortening of the period of fallow and the exhaustion of the soil. The time is drawing near when the country will no longer be able to produce its food on the usual system of unirrigated crops on burnt patches.[2] Yet when the swamps inland were brought under cultivation at the beginning of the twentieth century, this was the method adopted. They are now exhausted and have to be allowed to lie fallow. Only the swamp rice-fields which have been made continue to produce regularly. But there is still hope for Sierra Leone, for there are 500,000 acres of coastal marsh, only 60,000 of which are cultivated. If the cultivation of swamp rice becomes general, all difficulty over the food-supply will be removed.

This examination of West Africa has brought out various technical possibilities which will help cultivation to abandon the usual system of planting food crops on unirrigated burnt patches and will supply food to a larger population than the old system does. The use of the flooded ricefield, of plantations of trees, of irrigation, and of manure got from animals or any other source, and effective measures to check

[1] See the recent article by J. Dresch on 'La riziculture en Afrique occidentale' *Ann. de Géog.* 1949, pp. 295–312.
[2] C. J. Raes: 'Swamp Development in Sierra Leone' in *Farm and Forest*, Dec. 1941, p. 113.

soil erosion are the chief improvements by which it can be hoped to transform the usual system of agriculture in the tropics, that is to say, to get larger and steadier annual yields owing to the preservation of the soil.

Various experts aim at transforming the rural life of Africa south of the Sahara, by introducing mixed farming based on cultivation and livestock rearing. For instance, Auguste Chevalier[1] writes: 'When the negro cultivator is better educated, he will with the help of the agricultural bank be able to follow the French peasant by adopting a complex system of agriculture which will combine tilth with the rearing of livestock. He will live on a real farm surrounded by fields permanently under cultivation, ploughed, and hedged. He will have his livestock and fodder crops to feed his animals, and these will supply him with manure hitherto nearly unknown in Africa. He will no longer have to let his land lie fallow, and he will be able to devote himself to rational agriculture and rearing of livestock. In this way he will produce milk and butter, commodities which most tropical peoples are almost wholly without, though they are so good for children.' In fine, M. Aubréville[2] is strongly of the opinion that in areas of low rainfall, like the Sudan, the number of trees must be increased to give man fruit and animals leaves,[3] and especially to fix the soil with their roots. Hedges should be planted as windbreaks and to check æolian erosion. A condition of this progress is that annual bush-fires should cease. Many British experts share these views.[4]

This type of mixed farming is certainly not unknown in Africa south of the Sahara. We have seen that it exists among the Chaggas.[5] Besides, every negro village has its permanently cultivated fields. These are gardens around the villages and are fertilized with all the organic waste from the houses. The gardens are not always restricted to vegetables. Among the Mossis and Bobos (near Banfora or Korogo) they assume the appearance of veritable fields of sorghum or maize. In them permanent cultivation is not associated with deliberate manuring, but benefits from fertilizer which the villages cannot help giving. Interesting experiments have been made in encouraging the production of farm manure along with the rearing of livestock.[6]

It would, however, be mere delusion to seek the economic safety of tropical lands in an agricultural system imitated from temperate

---

[1] *L'agriculture coloniale*, Paris, 1942, p. 47.
[2] In a statement made in the course of a conversation with the author at Dakar on July 26, 1945.
[3] Especially *Acacia albida*, the leaves of which are relished by animals.
[4] J. H. Gisborne: 'Some Thoughts on Post-War Development' in *Farm and Forest*, April 1944, pp. 24–8.
[5] See above, p. 59.
[6] *Farm and Forest*, June 1944, p. 16 and Sept. 1944, p. 117; Dec. 1941, p. 106.

latitudes, that is, mixed farming consisting of the production of food in permanently cultivated unirrigated fields and the keeping of live-stock to provide labour, milk, and meat. It would be to forget that tropical soils are naturally of slight fertility and soon exhausted and that horned cattle do not find favourable conditions in the tropics, as much on account of the poor quality of the grass as of cattle diseases. With these reservations it is possible to imagine that mixed farming may afford a chance of raising the value of tropical lands, provided that the aim is clearly seen to be difficult to achieve and success to be dependent on the application of modern scientific processes which were not available in the traditional civilizations.[1] In most hot, wet lands livestock keeping will only be profitable after a scientific struggle against epizootic diseases, and the scientific knowledge for this is a modern acquisition.

In practice the difficulties are immense. Purely agricultural peoples must be given a liking for tending livestock. The animals must be protected from disease. Sound methods of using the dung must be developed. It is not enough to put the animals to graze in a field for the latter to be manured, for in the first place the livestock cannot stay long in a field where very little edible grass grows. Besides, in a tropical climate the animals' droppings are mostly lost, for the sun dries them, the wind disperses them in dust, termites eat them, and the heavy rain at the beginning of the wet season washes them away. Hence, the animals must be reared in stalls and the use of liquid manure sumps must be learnt together with the methods of preparing compost.

The use of the plough makes many experts seriously uneasy. Not merely do tropical soils not need to be deeply turned up, but they actually cannot stand it, for only the layer right next the surface has any agricultural value. If clumsily handled, the plough may cause erosion along its furrows.[2] Cases observed in Northern Nigeria and Uganda show that with his plough the cultivator can work a larger area, but that the tilth is not more intensive than that of the hoe. So in the end the clearings are needlessly large and thus compromise the future.

In districts where cattle-rearing is more or less impossible either from the fact that the climate is extremely favourable to the tsetse fly or because the population is too large for the smallest piece of

---

[1] For instance, it must not be forgotten that the substitution of pasture for a cultivated field is a delicate operation in temperate lands and must be carried out with care and skill, at least if it is expected to restore the fertility of the soil. It should be remembered that in large areas in France the increase of pastureland during the last few decades has not been an unmixed blessing for the soil through want of sufficient care. Furthermore, tropical cultivators know nothing of the methods of making and maintaining pasture.

[2] See below, p. 122.

25.
A Lugware woman hoeing the soil with a forked stick at Mahagi in Belgian Congo. With such a poor implement a vast deal of time and effort is wasted.

26.
The use of the mortar and pestle makes for slowness in the preparation of food. The photograph was taken in the outskirts of Elisabethville in Belgian Congo.

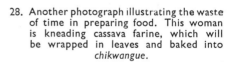

28. Another photograph illustrating the waste of time in preparing food. This woman is kneading cassava farine, which will be wrapped in leaves and baked into *chikwangue*.

7. More laborious preparation of food. The woman is opening palm nuts one by one.

29.
A primitive cassava press in
near Ubatura on the coa
the State of Sao Paulo, B

30.
Waste of time through poor methods
one of the causes of poverty and und
nourishment in the tropics. The man
husking beans at Aminbhavi ne
Dharwar, India.

31.
Primitive means of pre-
paring cassava *farinha* for
sale in Belem. On the right
is a press. Under the
shed are the grater and
the cauldrons in which the
farine is toasted.

land to be set aside as pasture, green manure can be an excellent remedy for soil exhaustion. Its use is being systematically observed in central Nigeria, where the leguminous *Mucuna utilis* seems important, but the wide spread of the use of green manure is far from being achieved. As for chemical fertilizers, they have to be carefully used in the tropics, which is yet another touch of inferiority as compared with temperate lands.

It does not seem very wise to lead tropical cultivators to use a system of agriculture like that of the French peasant. French farming is a legacy of the past and is ill adapted to the present state of method and economy. Are we sure that it is a good step to direct tropical farming towards a system of peasant proprietorship? It would perhaps be better to think of co-operative or collective farming. Which of the two systems is best suited to the present state of rural organization in the hot, wet regions is uncertain, and it is doubtful whether the choice lies with peasant proprietorship.

Clearly, agricultural methods are closely allied to agrarian systems and types of family organization. To change the agrarian system affects the family and the whole of the rest of the economic edifice. That does not shut out necessary reform, but yet reform should be carried out in the full knowledge of its economic and social consequences and also of its repercussion on the physical environment. Nothing useful can be achieved unless one envisages the problems of the soil, climate, health, forests, farming, land tenure, and society all together.[1]

Besides, the improvements proposed would only be practicable if those concerned, *i.e.* the tropical cultivators, felt a desire to apply them. But it is doubtful whether the cultivators are actuated by that desire, for they are encrusted with customs that are often rich in the wisdom of experience and they have no great desire to raise their standard of living. Unhealthy and ignorant, they are on the whole not ready for more work or for the reform of their methods. Hence, their economic system must be reorganized, and they must be given better health and an education which will make them realize the importance of economic improvement. Education and hygiene are more important than methods or processes.[2]

Granting this, the fact still remains that to seek improvement of these aspects by imitating European methods is perhaps to fall into a trap. Wherever the cultivation of swamp rice is possible, it is by far the best means of producing carbohydrates. It ensures good yields, avoids the need for fallow, prevents soil erosion, and ensures the

[1] H. C. Sampson and E. M. Crowther in *Technical Reports of the Leverhulme Trust: The West African Commission*, 1943; Fortes: 'Human Ecology in West Africa' in *African Affairs*, Jan. 1945, p. 27.

[2] See Gisborne's article referred to above, p. 95.

H

future.[1] Furthermore, by maintaining a vegetable mantle as nearly as possible like that of the natural forest, plantations of trees ensure good annual yields and safeguard the soil. It is in these two directions that hot, wet lands should direct their advance. Tropical Asia has pointed the way.

[1] For instance, in Dutch Guiana after various experiments with tobacco, sugar, cotton, cacao, coffee, bananas, and citrus fruit, swamp rice now seems to be the most promising crop (*Geog. Review*, 1943, p. 323). It is to be feared, however, that flooded ricefields in the uplands may be the source of malaria because the water is renewed (see below, p. 134, for the relation of tropical marsh fevers to running water), and must be so owing to the gradient, inevitable leaks, and permeability. Perhaps it is better to cultivate irrigated crops in specially favourable places, that is, at the bottom of alluvial valleys, and to let the soil dry periodically so as to kill the larvæ of the anopheles. There are, of course, varieties of rice that will tolerate this drying of the soil.

CHAPTER 10

HOT, WET ASIA

THE densely populated parts of tropical Africa and America occupy tiny areas and support a small total number of persons. India, Indo-China, and the East Indies, on the other hand, contain populations amounting to hundreds of millions.[1] It is as if mankind in the tropics can only go to the two extremes of sparse population on the one hand and excessive density on the other. How is the contrast to be explained? It is due not to physical, but to cultural conditions and arises through man's different reactions to similar physical conditions.

In this matter French Indo-China is a particularly interesting case because on the Tongking delta there is the greatest density of rural population in tropical Asia, because this density is of very long standing, and because it occurs in a land typical of the tropics.

French Indo-China has a hot, wet climate. Most of the country consists of mountains and low plateaus, its soil is generally very poor, and it is badly fever-ridden nearly all over. Out of a total area of 285,000 square miles and a population of 23 million persons a tract of 250,000 square miles contains only 4 million persons and has therefore a density of only 16 to the square mile. Vast expanses do not exceed 8 persons to the square mile. Out of the total area of 285,000 square miles crops occupy no more than 27,000 square miles, though the climate is never unfavourable to agriculture.

Low density of population occurs where the soil is cultivated on the *ray* (*ladang*) system, by burning a patch of the forest and planting maize or upland rice. By being cleared at regular intervals, the forest has on the whole become a secondary growth, and annual bush-fires have given rise to savanas. The natives who live by the *ray* system are poorly fed, suffer from annual food-shortage, and get things to sell and some of their food by collecting gum, valuable woods, mushrooms, etc., in the forest. None of these facts would be untrue in a description of a typical village in tropical Africa or America.

The low alluvial plains support 19 million persons on their 38,600 square miles. The Tongking delta[2] has 1,166 persons to the square mile on an area of 5,800 square miles. In some places the density

[1] The hot, wet regions in Asia have an area of 3 million sq. m. and a population of 530 millions. The hot, wet parts of America, Africa, Australia, and New Guinea have an area of $11\frac{1}{2}$ million sq. m. and a population of 170 million.

[2] For more details see P. Gourou: *Les paysans du delta tonkingois*, Paris, Les Editions d'Art et d'Histoire, 1936.

99

exceeds 3,630 persons to the square mile in rural districts. There is a great difference between the population on the plain and on the more or less broken relief around the delta. Within a few hundred yards a density of at least 400 or 500 persons to the square mile on the delta changes to a mere handful to the square mile, from over-population to almost void, from conditions specifically Asiatic to conditions typical of the tropics. The causes of this great difference can be given exactly and fitted most satisfactorily into the framework of tropical geography.

The rather poor soil on the delta is always of a good physical quality and never passes into laterite. As it is cultivable throughout, it responds well to human effort. The most fertile soil, that is, the most recent, on the banks of rivers or by the sea, is the most densely populated. Were the delta cultivated on the system of raising food crops without irrigation, but allowing the land an interval of fallow, it could not support a large population. It is, however, wholly used for swamp rice, which for 2,000 years has been giving good harvests every year. Many fields even yield two crops a year, whilst others add an unirrigated crop to the rice grown in the wet season. Swamp rice fosters economic stability, a dense population, and a high civilization; and it is the only cereal which can be cultivated year after year on the same soil in a tropical land and which gives adequate yields from poor soil so long as there is a suitable quantity of water.[1] Owing to its being planted out, rice occupies the soil for a relatively short time and gives two or even three crops a year. Nor does the soil deteriorate under swamp rice.

In Tongking the cereal is carefully and scientifically cultivated, and no effort is spared to increase the yield. It is easy to realize that a district which is wholly cultivated and produces two crops a year on 50 per cent. of its area should have an incomparably denser population than the surrounding country with its broken relief, in which the area under cultivation does not exceed 5 per cent. of the total and never gives more than one crop a year.

The large rural population on the plain is possible only because good agricultural methods and an improved social and political organization have been introduced from a higher civilization. This organization has enabled the dangerous floods of the Red River to be warded off by means of a network of dykes. In fact, but for the dykes

[1] The ricefield does best when well manured; but it is still profitable if poorly manured and even if it is not manured at all. This advantage is perhaps due to the fact that the algæ in the ricefield fix nitrogen. Besides, there is always manure enough for the seedbeds, and the young rice plants can before being planted out imbibe the elements needed for the growth of the grain. It is in fact very important for a crop to start on very fertile soil and for a plant to be able to absorb as soon as possible a large proportion of the elements it needs. (Sir A. Howard: *An Agricultural Testament*, O.U.P., 1943, p. 16.)

the usefulness of the delta would be reduced to almost nothing and the population could not be large. Drainage and irrigation have also required concerted planning.

The Annamites who live on the delta are sufficiently advanced to be able to solve these problems and for long ages have evinced great social stability. Has a high civilization arisen, therefore, and maintained itself in a tropical environment through mastering the cultivation of swamp rice? We cannot affirm this, for all the higher elements in Annamite civilization have come from China. The agricultural methods and the social and political organization are closely based on Chinese models. These cultural features have, therefore, been perfected outside the tropics and now flourish in this tropical district which lent itself to wholesale utilization through rice cultivation. But in the areas of broken relief around the delta a like utilization was impossible; and not only is its population sparser, but it is also less advanced in civilization. The difference in density corresponds exactly to a difference in physical conditions, both differences being due to the combined action of physical and cultural conditions.

There is little malaria on the Tongking delta, whilst the surrounding hill country is very unhealthy. The countryfolk know this well and are afraid of moving off the plain. Agricultural labourers working on plantations situated on the edge of the delta in the unhealthy area return every evening to sleep in their villages on the plain, so that by not spending the night on the plantation they may avoid being bitten by the anopheles. The healthiness of the delta is surprising at first sight, since the country is covered with flooded ricefields and ponds. Mosquitoes swarm in these, but the most dangerous anopheles are rare, because their larvæ do not like the muddy, stagnant water in ricefields and ponds.[1] The main arms of the Red River and its distributaries might in the dry season become a haunt of anopheles larvæ, because ribbons of water might meander along the beds and offer favourable quarters for them. But the land-hungry peasant cultivates the whole area uncovered at low water and does not let the streams follow a winding course. The river beds, both the smaller

[1] It has been observed in India (see *Nature*, March 30, 1940, p. 520) that the larvæ of the anopheles do not live in dirty water. Clean water can be prevented from being dangerous by being polluted with stale water from factories. It is also possible to throw into the water vegetable matter which on decaying will pollute the water and make it unwelcome to the larvæ. But Dr. Morin, the head of the Dalat Pasteur Institute, has observed sudden epidemics of malaria in villages on the Tongking delta. These coincide with an exceptionally large swarm of *Anopheles Sinensis*, an insect which usually feeds on animals. Are the epidemics due to special breeds of *A. Sinensis*? Or does an excessive swarm of the insects lead them to attack men? Should the possibility of malarial plasmodium being brought by persons returning from the hill country be considered?

dry season bed and the larger one in the wet season, are swept by the stream or the tide and are not dangerous.

Consequently, the healthiness of the delta is not due to natural causes. Man has achieved it by utilizing the whole area and controlling the water, that is, by substituting a completely tamed nature for a wild one. The improvement in healthiness is a by-product of complete utilization, and man has brought about the improvement unintentionally. More healthy conditions have followed on civilization, and, once assured, these new conditions have fostered a dense population. In its wild state the delta was certainly fever-stricken, for it must have been sufficiently supplied with clean, gently-flowing water to encourage the development of swarms of anopheles. In this case Nature has been content to bring together the physical conditions which, when utilized by civilized man with suitable agricultural methods and a satisfactory political organization, have led to the complete utilization of the soil, the disappearance of malaria, and the growth of a dense population. The civilized men in question were unable to utilize the hilly districts completely, since this would have been possible only to people with a scientific knowledge of malaria and capable of entering on an open and deliberate struggle against it.[1]

The civilization on the delta is helpless against malaria which develops in conditions not destroyed by the cultivation of the land. On the delta of the Songka (the plain of Vinh) terrible epidemics of malaria have been recorded during the season of the north-east monsoon. They are spread by *Anopheles Ludlowi*, the larvæ of which flourish near the shore in brackish pools where rainwater mingles with seawater thrown up by storm-waves from the north-east. Anopheles bred on the coast are carried inland by the wind. The traditional civilization on the delta could not overcome such extraordinary conditions, which could be remedied only by scientific study.

This explains why the delta is completely utilized and why it is densely populated. But how is it that rural density reaches an average of 1,160 persons per square mile and exceeds 2,500 over wide areas? How is it that 12, 24, 36 peasants live on one acre of cultivated land, whilst in Europe or North America there is one member of the agricultural community to an acre or even more?

Better yields from the land is not a satisfactory answer, for fields in

[1] Hence the amazing ethnographical patchwork in French Indo-China and other parts of Southeast Asia. As the traditional high civilization could flourish only on an alluvial plain which could be wholly utilized, districts presenting different characteristics of soil and relief could not be touched by that civilization and for this reason are backward. Hence the juxtaposition, to a degree not known in Europe, of peoples who practise different methods of cultivation, have reached very uneven stages in intellectual development, and possess quite different social and political institutions.

the tropics would have to produce 10 or 20 times more than those in the temperate belt, whereas the yield in cereals is far from being greater in the hot, wet lands. In very favourable cases like the good ricefields giving two crops a year on the lower Tongking delta, the total annual rice crop does not exceed 1 ton per acre. Consequently, this is a lower yield than that of the wheat grown on silty areas in Europe and of the rice harvested in *huertas* in Valencia or Emilia. Good land in Tongking giving one rice crop and one unirrigated crop does not yield more than between 4,000 and 4,500 lb. of grain a year.[1] The high yields from land in our temperate latitudes are certainly of recent date, and formerly part of the land was left fallow, whilst in Tongking the land has never rested. It follows therefore that in districts with large farming populations in Asia the crops were at one time greater than those in similar areas in Europe square mile for square mile. This advantage has disappeared today, but it was never great enough to explain the enormous difference in density to be seen in the rural populations of Europe and Southeast Asia. To say, as has often been done, that the tropical climate has given rise to the swarming humanity in southern Asia by allowing the soil to be cropped all through the year is a false conclusion from the evidence. On the contrary, it has been shown that nature in the tropics is probably an obstacle rather than a help to the development of a dense population. Enormously dense rural populations occur also in the temperate portions of China and Japan. They are a feature of the civilization.

A high birth-rate is not a sufficient cause of the enormous population. In rural districts in England and France the birth-rate was formerly very high, but it did not cause so great a density as occurs in the lowlands in tropical Asia. It may be thought that the peasants in Tongking have other resources besides agriculture, which enable them to live on an inadequate area of soil. Enquiry into the matter shows that the peasants display much ingenuity in seeking to increase their earnings by industry or commerce, but these activities are of little importance compared with agriculture. The great amount of labour needed in rice cultivation is not the cause of the great density of population, but is, on the contrary, probably a consequence. If during the busy periods the peasants all work in the fields, they are not employed on the average more than 125 days a year.

When all is said and done, great density of population is mainly associated with a low standard of food consumption and a material civilization based on the vegetable kingdom. The wants of the peasants in Tongking are very simple, which is one of the reasons why the population is so numerous. Besides, the people live on what they

[1] For further details, see above, p. 15.

produce. Though they feed simply, food represents between 70 and 80 per cent. of the value of what they 'consume.' In 1938 a peasant family of 4 or 5 persons spent no more than the equivalent of £5 a year. That is one-fiftieth of the expenditure of an agricultural labourer's family in England.

Peasants on the Tongking delta dress in cloth made of vegetable matter, build their houses of vegetable matter, use tools exclusively made of vegetable matter, and, above all, are mainly vegetarian in diet. Now, such a diet allows many more persons to live on a square mile of cultivated land than does a diet containing a good deal of animal products. The intermediary animal wastes most of the calories it absorbs.[1] Cow's milk and pig's flesh, which are the most profitable items in livestock keeping in that they present the least difference between the calories they give man and those needed to produce them, offer only one-sixth of what they have cost.[2] A vegetarian diet is not the outcome of a dense population, nor has it been adopted because the population has become so large. In parts of Indo-China where the population is sparse, the people have as strict a vegetarian diet as do the peasants on the Tongking delta. The diet is a cultural feature which should be regarded as a cause of the great demographic density.

The little plains in Annam repeat the features described in Tong-king and are in contrast with the sparsely peopled uplands of the Annamese mountains. The reason why Cochin China is less densely peopled is that the Annamites have been settled there only since the seventeenth century and have not had time to create the great population densities which characterize these people. Even in the fertile portions of the lower valley of the Mekong, the Cambodians are never in densely packed masses. The rather careless agricultural methods and their social and political institutions lend themselves less than those of the Annamites to the formation of densely peopled rural areas.

The conclusions which emerge from a study of French Indo-China and which can be applied to the whole of hot, wet Asia are as follows:—

Hot, wet Asia, which has a far larger population than other tropical regions, presents a juxtaposition of densely occupied areas

[1] For more details, see P. Gourou: *L'utilisation du sol en Indochine française*, Paris, 1940, pp. 192–6; and *La terre et l'homme en Extrême-Orient*, Paris, 1941, pp. 114–25.

[2] A very low standard of food consumption and a vegetarian diet produce the same results in other parts of the world. The density in the rural districts among the *huertas* in Valencia is 1,170 to the square mile and in the neighbourhood of Catania 1,110, whilst it rises to 1,680 in some parts of Campania (Melito di Napoli, Parete, Trentola, Lusciano, Frattaminore, Crispano).

and sparsely peopled expanses. The latter have physical and human characteristics similar to those in most hot, wet regions, *viz.* unhealthiness, poor and easily exhausted soil, unirrigated food crops grown on the *ray* system, and a sparse and backward population. Hence, the human peculiarity of hot, wet Asia lies in its densely peopled areas. The superabundant population in these is associated with good soil,[1] advanced social and political organization, intensive rice cultivation, and sound agricultural methods; in a word, with an advanced stage of civilization. The leaven of this civilization was brought from regions outside the tropics. Being wholly utilized, the densely peopled areas enjoy a healthiness far superior to that of tropical countries as a whole. The enormous rural population in hot, wet Asia is possible only with a very low standard of food consumption, and an almost exclusively vegetarian diet.

Siam and Burma are far less interesting than French Indo-China, because they have no plains with a superabundant population like that of the deltas in Tongking and northern Annam. As in Cochin China, the density of population is still low in their alluvial plains. Like the delta of the Mekong, the deltas of the Menam and Irrawaddy have only recently been settled and have not yet had time to become overcrowded. It is to this characteristic in common that these three plains owe the fact that they are the world's chief sources of rice-exports.

In India in 1941 out of a population of 389 million 87 per cent. lived in rural districts. Most of it is concentrated round the edges of the Deccan on fertile areas of recent alluvium, which either have a good rainfall or are easily irrigated. Rice cultivation is the chief means of earning a living in these plains (see Fig. 13). The density of population on the Ganges delta increases from west to east with the rainfall and the relative importance of rice cultivation. This part of Bengal is the largest area of dense population in India. In 1931 the Dacca district had 1,060 persons to the square mile on its 2,700 square miles and the subdivision of Munshiganj had 2,380. The coast plain fringing the peninsula on the east is a continuous ribbon of high population density. In Orissa, for instance, the density on the delta of the Mahanadi averages 620 and exceeds 1,300 downstream from

---

[1] The question arises: Are the alluvial plains built up in the sea at the mouths of Asiatic rivers not more fertile than those due to African or American rivers? The Red River, Mekong, Irrawaddy, Brahmaputra, and Ganges get a good deal of their water and alluvium from regions outside the tropics. Is not this a cause of fertility? Even above its inner delta the Niger carries little load and its water contains a very small amount of matter in solution. A comparative study of the soil of the maritime delta of the Niger and the Ganges delta would be of great interest. As for the Nile in Egypt, it owes the relative fertility of its waters to the run-off in sub-arid regions.

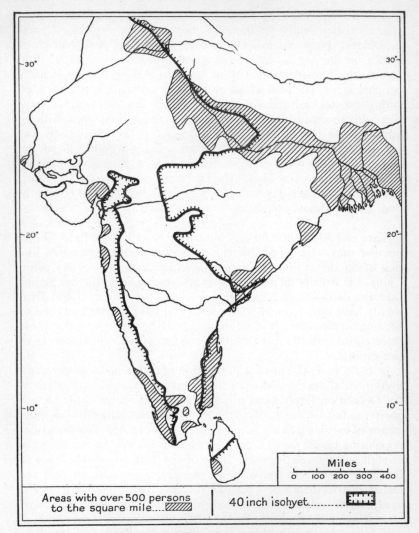

FIG. 13.   Rainfall and population in India

Cuttack. On the west the coast strip is still more densely peopled, especially in Travancore and Cochin. In 1931 Cochin averaged 1,800 to the square mile and greatly exceeded 2,600 in some districts.

The hilly regions are far less densely peopled and are often inhabited by backward tribes. Instances of this are seen in the Vindhya Mountains to the north of the Nerbada and the Mahadeo Hills to the south, the upper valley of the Sone to the east of Jubbalpore, and the Dewodi Munda, Nilgiri, and Cardamom Hills. The difference between the densely and sparsely peopled areas is often striking. It is nowhere better marked than in the Terai at the foot of the Himalayas, which is so fever-stricken as to be almost uninhabitable.

The districts which are densely peopled owing to complete utilization are less fever-stricken than the others. The southern and eastern portions of the Bengal delta are healthy; but on the other hand malaria has spread in western Bengal since the end of the nineteenth century and has caused a decrease in the population. Western Bengal lies on the fringe of the delta, and, in Burdwan, valleys filled with recent alluvium mingle with terraces of ancient alluvial deposits. Now, over the latter brooks run down a steep gradient and make lodgings favourable to the anopheles. It is accepted that in other places malaria is dangerous on the fringes of deltas. In Orissa, for instance, the narrow south and north ends of the delta are more fever-stricken than the rest of the plain. As in other districts the recent clearing of the jungle from the alluvial terraces has caused an increase of the most dangerous of mosquitoes, the anopheles, since these insects like light. It is also pointed out that on the ancient terraces the irrigation tanks have been less well maintained than in the past owing to an unfortunate change in the system of cultivation which has worsened the lot of the peasants. The tanks, which were constructed by damming little valleys, are not dangerous if deep and clean at the banks; but if through want of care the banks are badly kept and if the tanks themselves become sloughs with slowly moving water, the anopheles find conditions favourable. A falling-off in the crops and an increase in malaria go hand in hand, each acting on the other. Underfed human beings are an easy prey to malaria. It has been said that in Burdwan the Muslims are probably less subject to malaria than the Hindus, because they eat meat.[1]

The western fringe of Bengal formed an excellent starting-place for the spread of malaria just at a time when conditions favourable to the progress of the disease were developing on the western delta itself. In the sixteenth century the waters of the Ganges almost stopped flowing through the western arm, the Baghirati (whose mouth is the Hooghly), to run into the Brahmaputra through the Padma. The results were disastrous. There was no longer as much water as before for the flooding of the ricefields; the deposition of fertilizing mud ceased; and the main channels of the streams were no longer swept by a strong current and so became favourable haunts for the anopheles. The same kind of thing was observed in Ceylon in 1933 when the streams ceased to sweep their channels because prolonged drought

[1] A. Geddes: *La civilisation du Bengale occidental et ses facteurs géographiques* Montpellier, 1927.

weakened the current. Lastly, the attraction of Calcutta has given rise to a close network of railway lines and embanked roads; and owing to lack of care the drainage system has been upset and irrigation impaired. Hence, there are many causes of increased attacks of malaria, but all of them, whether physical or human, indicate a falling-off in the area under cultivation.

The people of India use intensive agricultural methods, though they show less care than the Vietnamese (Annamites) in making use of manure. The alluvial soil in Uttar Pradesh (United Provinces) has for a thousand years been yielding moderate crops unmanured. It is very minutely cultivated, which is what has enabled this result to be obtained; but the yield would be much greater if the Hindus would consent to the use of human excreta and did not use cow dung as fuel.

India is endowed with a high civilization, which seems inferior to the old Chinese culture as far as political and administrative institutions are concerned, but which was and is splendid and capable of answering the social and intellectual needs of dense populations. But much of the civilization comes from without—perhaps the better parts. The Aryan invasion, Sanscrit, the caste system, Indo-Greek art, Islam, and very many other features emphasize the importance of cultural elements introduced from Mesopotamia and Persia. The system and practice of government established in India by the English and destined never to disappear wholly, is yet another valuable foreign contribution to culture.[1] In fact, like all other tropical countries, India has received a great deal from the rest of the world and has given little in return. Germs of culture from lands outside the tropics have been needed to develop a high civilization in this hot, wet country.

Lastly, here as in French Indo-China, high rural densities of population cannot be explained without taking into account the low standard of food consumption and the vegetarian diet. In spite of her 214 million horned cattle, India feeds almost exclusively on vegetable matter.[2]

These features conform with those common to the human geography of hot, wet lands as described above. But India offers a special peculiarity. The peninsular plateau, which is far from being an alluvial plain and is fairly high, moderately varied in relief, and formed of rocks mantled in poor and often lateritic soil, has on the whole a rather high density of population of two or three score, and in places 250 persons to the square mile. The fact is partly explained by the large extent of very quiet relief on the Deccan, the

---

[1] India also owes to European influence the rapid increase in her population during recent years. But this is no decided advantage. See below, p. 127.
[2] See above, p. 65.

really hilly portions being almost uninhabited. Besides, flooded rice-fields cover part of the plateau, since water for irrigation is supplied by countless 'tanks.' Thus, an agricultural system perfected on alluvial plains has been established on the plateau owing to the control of water. We have seen that properly maintained tanks are not lodging for the larvæ of the anopheles. On the contrary, tanks and swamp rice cultivation are excellent means of eliminating malaria. Lastly, vast expanses of the north-western Deccan have a fertile soil, called *regur*, which can be tilled without being allowed to rest by reverting to forest. The origin of *regur* is still not well known. Very probably the type of soil is to some extent associated with a rather dry climate having a rainfall of between 20 and 40 inches, for a greater amount would long since have leached out the bases contained in the soil. Hence, this type of country is to be found on the borders of the hot, wet regions.

In Indonesia contrasts in density of population are frequent. In 1940 Java and Madura had 940 persons to the square mile, whilst Sumatra (see Fig. 15) and Celebes had 17 and Borneo 3. Java's superiority is of long standing, but asserted itself in an extraordinary manner during the nineteenth century. In fact, the island contained only 96 persons to the square mile in 1817; and there is no other instance in the world of a purely rural population multiplying so fast unaided by immigration.

Java has very fertile basic volcanic soil. But its quality is not a sufficient explanation of the astonishing density of population, since the greatest concentrations are found on non-volcanic soil. The island has remarkable facilities for irrigation. But the main factor in high population densities must be sought in the civilization. First of all, the old Indo-Javanese civilization, whose higher elements had been brought in from outside, contributed the political and social framework and the intellectual development. Besides, European influence due to the Dutch ensured economic progress and permitted the extraordinary increase in population. It had also added the most prosperous plantation system in the world to the resources of swamp rice cultivation developed by the old Javanese civilization.[1]

The greatest rural density in Java is reached on the north coast plain, where in 1930 in the district of Adiwerno it was 4,240 persons to the square mile over an area of 36 square miles. For an area of that size this is probably the greatest rural density in the world. In 1931 the canton of Tra Lu on the Tongking delta had a density of 4,270, but only on 8 square miles. At Adiwerno the soil is not volcanic. It is only moderately fertile, but, being of a good physical

[1] For the plantation system, see below, p. 133.

texture, is complete utilized. Not a square inch of land is uncultivated, and owing to a rational system of irrigation the harvests are regularly reaped. Swamp rice cultivation is the main occupation, but many peasants spend more or less time working on sugar-cane plantations run by Europeans. Consequently the European commercial system plays an important part.[1]

The Philippines would afford no peculiar features worthy of mention in this rapid sketch, did not swamp rice cultivation among the Igorots have a very special character.[2] This tribe has made irrigated ricefields some 1,500 feet up on the hillsides in the mountains of north-western Luzón. The construction and upkeep of their tiny irrigated terraces on slopes so steep as to be more suitable for forest requires infinite care. But though excellent cultivators of rice, the Igorots use many clumsy processes and are rather backward in civilization. They have no metal implements, and their hoes are wooden; yet they can forge weapons. The plough is unknown to them. They skilfully irrigate their ricefields by using the gradients of streams, but they know of no process for raising water. If a ricefield cannot be irrigated by means of a conduit, it is watered laboriously by carrying the liquid to the field in small pots. The Igorots are, or were, headhunters; they are ignorant of writing and have no political organization higher than that of the village. All the evidence points to the Igorots having been familiar with swamp rice cultivation before the use of the plough spread among cultivators in Southeast Asia. In spite of all the primitive aspects of their civilization, the Igorots succeed in reaching a population density of 180 to the square mile. This is due to the cultivation of swamp rice, and this in spite of the fact that the Igorots do not live on an alluvial plain and are not high on the scale of civilization. Yet the Igorot system of rice cultivation must not be taken as a pattern for imitation in mountainous regions in the hot, wet belt, since it requires an enormous outlay of human effort, an outlay that is possible only if the standard of living is very low and man's labour regarded as of little worth.

The case of tropical Asia proves that in hot, wet regions dense patches of population may develop with hundreds of millions of people. The application of Asiatic agricultural methods, especially in

[1] Intensive cultivation of unirrigated fields (*tegalan*) is also practised in Java and Madura by means of a judicious use of stable and green manure and of a rotation consisting of upland rice, tubers, groundnuts, and vegetables. But it is almost exclusively hoe cultivation and can be nothing else. Should the standard of living rise, food crops could not continue to be grown on the *tegal* system.

[2] F. M. Keesing: *Population and Land Utilization among the Lepanto*, International Geographical Congress, Amsterdam, 1938, *Colonial Geography*, pp. 458–64. See also Daryll Forde: *Habitat, Economy and Society*, London, 1939, p. 392.

rice cultivation, together with peace and the public services ensured by stable government might in similar physical conditions have the same results in America and Africa as in Asia. This would indeed be only a renewal in our own times of the process by which civilizing influences were transferred in the course of ages to the countries in tropical Asia.

The development of the patches of sparse population which occur between the densely peopled areas in Southeast Asia raises the same problems as it does in other hot, wet lands, *viz.* health and economics. Such lands must be made healthy before being peopled, and to people them would call for the improvement of productive processes suited to them. In many of these territories the soil is too poor to warrant the slightest attempt to utilize it. But Southeast Asia has the great advantage of possessing large human populations suitable for becoming the colonists essential to the development of soil that is of any use at all.

The densely populated parts of tropical Asia have their special problems. These are not problems of development, but on the contrary are due to over-population. First of all comes the rise in the standard of living. Of course, this does not mean that the standard of living among people in the sparsely populated districts is satisfactory or that raising it is undesirable. But the terms of the problem are not the same in the two types of region. In sparsely peopled countries the first step is to make the place healthy and to change the methods of using the soil, to pass from the *ladang* to more profitable systems; whilst in over-populated regions such measures either have no point or else are of secondary importance. The exact meaning of over-population is, of course, open to much dispute. Should the term refer to a district with more people than it can feed, or one which cannot ensure a reasonable amount of work for all its inhabitants?[1]

Various measures can be used to raise the standard of living in over-populated districts. But these means will be effective only if the population ceases to increase its total. Owing to the advance of medical science, the death-rate has greatly declined in the past hundred years, whilst the birth-rate has been kept at a level to which it had been raised by communities needing a large number of children in order not to die out. This is a mediæval birth-rate with a modern death-rate. How can emigration or industrial development absorb the surplus population in India, if it persists in increasing by 5 million persons a year? Very many parts of Southeast Asia have exceeded the optimum population. A real improvement in the standard

[1] For a more detailed examination of this question, see P. Gourou: *L'utilisation du sol en Indochine française*, 1940, pp. 431–3.

of living among the rural population would need a decrease in numbers. By employing processes requiring less labour, fewer agricultural workers would secure a higher production and would thus have a higher standard of living than at present. Once achieved, a decrease in the number of labourers would demand a substantial drop in the birth-rate, the occupation of a large number of country folk in industry, and the settlement of more people by adequate methods in sparsely peopled areas.[1] And this would all be very difficult to bring about.

The raising of the quantity of food available for those who remain cultivators will depend on whether the gross returns from the land are increased by growing the most paying crops, by plant selection, and by the use of better manure, and on whether the cultivator's net return is increased by means of the break-up of large estates, the suppression of usury, and the introduction of co-operative measures.

[1] For the problem of the settlement of Tongkingese in Cochin China, see P. Gourou: *L'utilisation du sol en Indochine française*, pp. 148–51.

…e rich ricefields at the bottom of the …ley are in strong contrast with the …or soil on the slopes. The latter have …en denuded by thoughtless cultivation … well as by erosion. Notice that the …pe in the foreground is cut by a gully … and covered with lateritic gravel.

…cefields to the south-west of Calcutta. …e fields are flooded from canals. Note … fish-fence, the fisherman's shelter, …d the canoe made by hollowing out the trunk of a palm tree.

34. Ploughing flooded ricefields near Pondicherry, India.

35. Rice cultivation on the Tongking delta near Hanoi. The woman is scooping water from a ditch into a ricefield. On the left is a pond containing water for household purposes. In the background are a water buffalo and a clump of bamboos. The district contains 1,300 persons to the square mile.

CHAPTER 11

PROBLEMS DUE TO EUROPEAN INTERVENTION IN HOT, WET LANDS

EUROPEAN intervention has had immense consequences, especially in countries typical of the tropics—that is, those that are sparsely peopled and backward in civilization. In densely peopled areas European intervention has had less effect, for in such countries problems of development have not arisen, and the more civilized native communities have been less easily influenced.

The outcome of European activities has in many cases been disastrous to the natural wealth and the native peoples. Lack of understanding of environmental conditions affecting both Europeans and natives has caused mistakes and failures; but the experience of these regrettable incidents should not be lost, and the lessons learnt from them should guide future European action in the tropics.

There is no need to go deeply into the problem of white settlement in hot, wet lands. Thrilling in itself, it is of limited interest, for there is not a great deal of such settlement:[1] nor does it seem destined to increase. An immense amount of written evidence has been collected on the subject,[2] but no definite conclusions have been reached. Two conflicting schools exist, one asserting that the hot, wet climate soon wears down Europeans, the other that this climate has nothing like the disastrous effect attributed to it.

In reality, it is the environment that matters, not the climate, for the heat and damp of the tropics cannot be proved to have by themselves a great effect on the European, since he can live, work with his hands, and beget strong children in a tropical climate. The environment does not consist of the climate alone, but also of tropical diseases, agricultural conditions, and the native population. A white people could flourish in a hot, wet region, were it quite healthy, were there no natives, and were the soil of lasting fertility. But none of these conditions is easily realized, and it is even more difficult to find them all three together.

Tropical diseases strictly limit the number, natural increase, and activities of Europeans as well as of the natives. They are especially dangerous for settlers if the country has natives to act as sources of

---

[1] Except in Brazil; see below, p. 116.
[2] Clearly summed up by Sorre in *Les fondements biologiques de la géographie humaine*, Paris, 1943, 440 pp. See also Grenfell Price: 'White settlers in the Tropics,' *Amer. Geog. Soc.*, 1939, p. 193.

virus. The presence of natives introduces another danger, a social one, for if Europeans dominate a native community, they become an aristocracy and direct the labour of the natives, who then form the lower classes. Such a system has drawbacks, the first of which is that it relieves the Europeans of all physical effort, though exercise is even more indispensable in the tropics than in a temperate region; secondly, the Europeans form an incomplete community with all the defects inherent in an idle class. Lastly, the Europeans are bound to become half-castes, for creole communities do not last. But climate has nothing to do with the matter.

A European population can till the soil with its own hands in a hot, wet country and produce its own food. But the natural infertility and instability of the soil affects European peasants as well as natives, and there is no reason why the former should have a higher standard of living than the latter. The ample life of the colonist is possible only because of the employment of a large amount of native labour. Europeans have no very great reason to be led into making real colonies in hot, wet lands, since, except where the conditions of life in the country of origin are especially wretched, European peasants in the tropics will have a lower standard of living than that existing in rural districts in temperate latitudes.

Every actual case confirms these general views. The Republic of Costa Rica[1] contains about 400,000 whites out of a population of 570,000 on some 20,000 square miles. They are petty farmers living for the most part above the 3,000 foot contour in the *tierra templada* and so do not belong to the hot belt. Yet there are large groups of whites far lower down on the Puntarenas and Guanacaste ranches and in the Digris valley. These whites are not degenerate, but have a very low standard of living. They are lucky enough to live in a district in which cattle are not exposed to the epizootic diseases that ravage the hot, wet parts of Africa; nor is there any problem arising from the presence of a native population.

Puerto Rico and Cuba are good examples of successful European colonization in hot, wet lands. The inhabitants are mainly of European origin, and Puerto Rico has 544 persons to the square mile, whilst Cuba has 112. But the environment is relatively healthy, as it is throughout the West Indies. The European settlers came from countries with a very low standard of living, and the standard of living is not very high today among the colonists. Nor is the population pure white. Cuba and, still more so Puerto Rico, are placed in an artificial economic situation[2] since their sugar has a privileged market in the United States. Like all the West Indies, these two large

[1] L. Waibel: 'White Settlement in Costa Rica' in *Geog. Review*, 1939, p. 529.
[2] See below, p. 125.

islands tend towards the plantation system and import a good proportion of the food they eat. From the economic point of view this arrangement is preferable to local production of food on the *ladang* system.[1]

The Europeans in the Panama Canal Zone are in a splendid state of health, and the annual death rate is only 6·36 per thousand. True, the population consists wholly of young people; yet adults and children look magnificently healthy. They do not suffer from the equatorial climate, though many of the men do heavy physical labour. The fact is that tropical diseases have been wholly wiped out, and the people enjoy a high degree of comfort and a perfect diet. But these employees of the Canal live in artificial economic conditions, since they are maintained by American money and do not wholly depend on the country in which they live.[2]

The Scotch and Irish who in the seventeenth century settled in the island of Saba in the Lesser Antilles have kept their racial purity,[3] and have not degenerated. But the island is healthy, and to its meagre resources the inhabitants have added high pay earned in the United States Navy, in which large numbers of them serve. Similarly, the descendants of English and Scottish settlers in the Cayman Islands (dependencies of Jamaica) are in splendid condition. Mr. Billmayer[4] who has studied the facts, does not hesitate to write that these Europeans in the Caymans are probably 'better in physique and health, and of sharper intelligence than the average American,' though they live in lat. 19° 20′ N. But there are no tropical diseases, and the inhabitants earn a large part of their living by turtle-fishing (exporting the turtles to the United States) and by wages earned on English and American merchant ships.

On the other hand, the Surinam Dutch live merely by tilling the soil. They are poor, but not degenerate, and the women remain very fertile. The Pomeranians who settled on both the plateau and the hot lowlands in the Brazilian State of Espirito Santo between 1847 and 1862 form a community full of vitality, but with a standard of living below that of German peasants.

In northern Queensland the coast strip is really hot and rainy; yet on it pure whites cultivate sugar cane with their own hands. The

---

[1] For example, in Cuba during the years 1937–9 the ratio of production to consumption was as follows: sugar 1,643 per cent.; tobacco 260 per cent.; pineapples 190 per cent.; tomatoes 158 per cent.; bananas 140 per cent.; coffee 136 per cent.; rice 5 per cent.; wheat 0 per cent.; beans 66 per cent.; oil 33 per cent. (*Geog. Review*, 1943, p. 501.)

[2] Grenfell Price: 'White Settlement in the Panama Canal Zone' in *Geog. Review*, 1935, pp. 1–11.

[3] Grenfell Price: 'White Settlement in Saba Island, Dutch West Indies,' in *Geog. Review*, 1934, pp. 42–60.

[4] J. H. S. Billmayer: 'The Cayman Islands' in *Geog. Review*, 1946, pp. 29–43.

exclusively white population of the sugar belt amounted to 251,000 in 1939, and the people are in perfect health, the birthrate being no lower than it is in the rest of Australia. But there are no tropical diseases, no malaria, dysentery, ankylostomiasis, etc., nor is there a single aboriginal in the sugar belt. The kanakas who were 'imported' formerly to work in the canefields and who might have been sources of infection were all sent home to satisfy the requirements of the White Australia Policy. The standard of living among the white agricultural workers in Queensland is satisfactory, but it rests on the plantation system and, above all, it depends on artificial conditions, for in 1939 when the price of sugar on the world-market was £7 19s. a ton, it was £24 2s. a ton, or three times the world price, on the Australian market.

In fine, these various white colonies have been placed in exceptional economic or health conditions. Where such conditions do not exist, the white colonists have at best a very poor standard of living. It is therefore wise to conclude that there is no future for white colonization in hot, wet lands.

The case of Brazil clearly shows the vicissitudes to which white colonization is subject if it does not respect the limitations imposed by the tropical environment. The 44 million Brazilians certainly have a large proportion of Indian and Negro blood. But this does not mean that Brazil is not to be regarded as a European colony. European predominance in the racial components is beyond doubt, and furthermore the culture is European. In these circumstances experience in Brazil is very instructive (see Fig. 2, p. 3).

The basis of the white population consists of Europeans who had had a very low standard of living in their native land and were not surprised at the low yield of crops in the tropics. The first settlers were in fact Portuguese who came at the beginning of the seventeenth century from the poor and over-populated mountains of northern and central Portugal and from the Azores, which were no more productive. A fundamental condition of successful white settlement in hot, wet lands was thus fulfilled.

When confronted with the natural conditions the settlers reacted in the same way as the natives had done. For food production the first to arrive resorted to collecting or to burnt-patch cultivation, that is, to the *roça* system. As they were Europeans belonging to a trading civilization, collecting was mainly directed to a search for produce intended for export. The produce demanded of the *caboclo* varied in the course of centuries according to the needs of commerce,[1] but consisted at first of logwood ('Brazil wood') got from the forests

[1] P. Deffontaines in *Ann. de Géog.*, 1939, p. 389.

on the north-east coast, cravo bark, ipecacuanha root, rubber, matë leaves, oil-yielding babassú nuts, Brazil nuts, mangabeira gum, oiticica oil, the poisonous timbó, balata gum, tonka beans, urucury wax, fan palm wax, palissandre oil, copahu oil, ucuhuba wax, etc. Collecting is a very attractive business. In the seventeenth century the sugarcane plantations in Maranhão were abandoned in favour of gathering cacao beans and cravo bark, and in the nineteenth century the fields in the district of Belem in Pará were deserted in favour of rubber collection. Some collectors are unable to return to agriculture if collecting ceases to be profitable. When the people on the Rio Negro were ruined by the slump in rubber, they did not resign themselves to growing food crops, but in 1933 still depended on imported food (beans and dried fish and meat). As the diet contained nothing fresh, it contributed to the ill health of the population, which nevertheless did not turn over to agriculture.[1] The collecting mentality is certainly one of the most serious obstacles to a spontaneous trend towards intensive agriculture and stability in the economic system of the Amazon region.

Cultivators of European origin practise a shifting cultivation on burnt patches. It is doubtful whether they invented it for themselves or borrowed it from the Indians.[2] Be this as it may, the settlers have adopted the simplest agricultural system indicated by the natural conditions. Nor could they use any other system to grow maize and beans which they took as the basis of their diet. But the standard of living of the patch-burning peasant is very low and by no means higher than that of other inhabitants of the hot, wet belt. German settlers in Espirito Santo are no better off than a negro on the Guinea coast or a Javanese peasant. *Caboclos* are even known to procure weapons from the Indians. The utensils used by the inhabitants of the middle valley of the São Francisco are primitive and consist chiefly of paraffin tins and calabashes.[3] Yet owing to their European origin and the absence of trypanosomiasis among animals, the

---

[1] E. Hanson in *Geog. Review*, 1933, p. 597.

[2] It should be noticed that the *roça* system is not unknown in central Portugal. The peasants in the Alemtejo cut down the vegetation and burn it before sowing seed. The cycle is one year of tilth to between eight and twenty years' fallow. See Orlando Ribeiro: *Le Portugal central*, a guide-book for Excursion C (central Portugal) of the International Geographical Congress at Lisbon in 1949, pp. 84–5. However, as the cultivated plants are native (maize, cassava, and beans) and as the first Portuguese settlers took Indian wives, it is probable that the *roça* system, which is still responsible for the food-supply of the greater part of the population of Brazil, was taken over from the Indians.

[3] R. E. Crist: 'Cultural Crosscurrents in the Valley of the Rio São Francisco' in *Geog. Review*, 1944, pp. 587–612. Just outside the town of São Paulo fair-complexioned peasants of German origin show marks of great degeneration (Parelheiros, a colony in the county of Santo Amaro). Those in Guareí (north-west of Itapetininga) are no better. Strangely enough, the names Moreau, Dubois, Briquet, and Augereau appear among the peasants in Ubatuba on the coast of the State of São Paulo.

Brazilian settlers rear cattle, though the beasts are of poor quality because of the unsuitability of the tropics for rearing livestock. Particularly primitive forms of livestock rearing are to be seen on the northern slopes of Itatiaya.[1]

The colonization of Brazil was accompanied by remarkable restlessness. Thousands of peasants would leave their districts because they were attracted to other regions in the hope of making a fortune quickly, of finding a *bonanza*, that is, the profits from some produce collected, the discovery of mineral wealth (gold, diamonds, and emeralds in Minas Geraes during the eighteenth century, when 500,000 persons must have left the north-east), the popularity of the new plantations, and the lure of high wages in the factories built just then at São Paulo. Others fled merely because they were forced to do so by catastrophic droughts. For instance, the droughts in Ceará pushed the inhabitants towards the Amazon region. The call of a *bonanza* sometimes acted like a panic. In the middle valley of the São Francisco peasants abandoned clearings planted with cassava to follow the stream of emigrants. The crops were lost and the price of cassava rose locally. The restlessness thus displayed was due to many causes,[2] but chief among them were the rapid exhaustion of the soil and the poverty of the cultivators, both of which are of normal occurrence in the hot, wet belt. Only in southern Brazil is there any sign of men's taking root and of the formation of a real peasantry, a development due to many factors, all of which are, however, controlled and guided by the cooler, drier southern environment.[3]

Until recently the manner in which plantations were run in Brazil greatly contributed to the ruin of the soil, for the aim was to produce goods for export. Hence, agriculture was commercial and not intended for subsistence. The planters wanted immediate returns and had no wish to ensure a supply of foodstuffs for future generations. They did not observe the code of wise precautions which is the basis of the agricultural system in the hot, wet regions. Brazilian peasants themselves state the matter thus: 'For twelve hours we do the land as much harm as possible. But during the other twelve we sleep, and then God and the land put things right again.' This is, furthermore, a

[1] P. Deffontaines in *Revue de Géog. alpine*, 1937, p. 505.

[2] In his 'Mémoire sur le système d'agriculture adopté par les Braziliens, et les résultats qu'il a eus dans la province de Minas Geraes,' *Mémoires du Museum d'Hist. nat.*, vol. 14 (1827), pp. 85–93, August de Saint-Hilaire as early as 1827 wrote of the people of Minas Geraes: 'They are ever ready to sacrifice the most positive reality for the figments of their imagination. Most of them have left their birthplaces and have several times moved this way or that with their families, property, and slaves. . . . The destruction of the woods is not the only unfortunate result of this system. A small population becomes more difficult to control when it scatters over an immense area, and by living at long distances apart the cultivators gradually lose the components of civilization.'

[3] From an article by P. Monbeig in *Ann. de Géog.*, 1937, pp. 278–99.

characteristic display of Brazilian optimism. The economic history of the country shows a series of plantations giving excellent results at first, but ending in the ruin of the land they occupy. Thus, there was the sugarcane period in the Pernambuco district during the seventeenth and eighteenth centuries, the tobacco period in Bahía in the eighteenth century, and the coffee period now apparently in its decline. The coffee bush seems to be retreating before cotton, oranges, and cocoa.[1] The Parahyba district in the eastern part of the State of São Paulo has become depopulated, the *cafezals* having deserted it after ruining the soil.[2] The forest does not grow again on these devastated areas, and the savana which takes its place is used only to a slight degree for rearing cattle on an extensive system. Cattlemen from Minas Geraes buy or rent the land: '*Mineiro traz consigo o deserto.*' For instance, in 1940 the *bairro* of Pedra Negra in the county of Taubaté had a dozen houses, a chapel, and a shop. In 1946 the whole area was grass-grown and the houses were empty and going to ruin. In 1929 the *povoação* of Entre Montes to the north-east of Campinas had a population of three or four hundred. In 1946 it had only thirty persons. Similarly, the Vale do Camanducaia on the borders of São Paulo and Minas Geraes and once upon a time containing a wealth of coffee bushes and a good population is now in a demographic decline. Pasture is replacing not only coffee, but also the *roça* or traditional agriculture of the peasants. This is happening in Cunha, a county too cool for coffee growing. In damp bottoms swamp rice cultivation is beginning and may prove to be the start of economic recovery on a sound basis. Though the cocoa plantations in the south of the State of Bahía are primitive, yet they are well adapted to the environment since they keep a forest cover.

The case of Brazil affords many lessons for Europeans and their plantation system, but the teaching is rather negative. The systems which ensure the greatest yield per acre, regular annual production, and continued preservation of the soil on tree plantations are found elsewhere, namely, in the plantations in Southeast Asia.[3]

Tropical conditions can only be commanded by being obeyed. It is by not knowing this principle that European intervention in hot,

[1] The facts are particularly well seen in the *Baixada Fluminense*, where there has been a succession of different crops since the seventeenth century. The disappearance of sugarcane plantations in the *reconcavo* of Guanabará has resulted in the abandonment of the district and the establishment of complete marsh conditions owing to the blocking of the drainage. See the fine treatise by Dr. Renato da Silveira Mendes: *Paisagens Culturais da Baixada Fluminense* (a thesis for a doctorate in the University of São Paulo, 1948, 228 pp., typewritten, with numerous maps and diagrams).

[2] P. E. James: 'The Changing Pattern of Population in São Paulo State,' in *Geog. Review*, 1938, p. 353.

[3] See below, p. 137.

wet regions has only too often done serious harm to nature and man. Some of the damage has been due simply to greed. But some has been the unforeseen and unforeseeable consequence of the entry of the European into hot, wet countries.

Among the unintentional misdeeds a chief place must be given to the spreading of tropical and other diseases. Scientists in general agree in thinking that yellow fever is of African provenance and was carried by negro slaves to America, where it has been a scourge.[1] American malaria specialists are inclined to think that the most serious form of marsh fever, tropical malaria, was imported into America in the same way. The propagation of insect-carriers may also be the work of man. *Anopheles Gambiæ*, an African mosquito which is a terrible carrier of malaria, was not found until 1930 in the Brazilian town of Natal. It multiplied so fast that in 1938 nine-tenths of the inhabitants of the country around Natal were malarial.[2] Smallpox, spread by European prospectors and missionaries, has certainly helped to decrease the population of the Amazon region. Lung diseases and smallpox brought by Europeans have also played havoc among the Polynesians.

In 1875 some 40,000 persons, or 28 per cent. of the population, died in Fiji from an epidemic of measles brought by the crew of a European ship. In Africa, that paradise of tropical diseases, European intervention has spread sleeping-sickness. Exact data[3] prove that the Nambikwara Indians were almost wiped out by diseases brought by Europeans. When their country was explored by General Rondon in 1915, the Nambikwara numbered about 10,000. Today there are only 2,000 or 3,000 of them. In 1927 influenza killed one group of them, and in 1929 another epidemic of influenza killed 300 persons in two days.

The action of the economic world today may be unintentionally disastrous. The tremendous boom and subsequent abandonment of certain kinds of wild crops has been baneful to tropical lands. Frantic gathering of rubber in the Amazon and Congo regions created no wealth and left ruin when it ended. Attracted by the demands of European commerce, natives may unwisely extend some export crop.

[1] See above, p. 10. The discovery of dormant forms of yellow fever in America may have led to a belief in its American origin; but dormant forms occur far and wide in Africa.

[2] In 1938 a very violent epidemic of malaria broke out in Baixa Verde in Rio Grande do Norte, causing the death of at least 20,000 out of 100,000 cases. Energetic and effective steps led to the destruction of *A. Gambiæ* in the Natal district. And it was time too, for the situation would have become very serious if *A. Gambiæ* had been able to spread into rainier districts, for the mosquito had not found the conditions most favourable to its development in the climate of Natal, where there is a dry season of eight months.

[3] C. Levi-Strauss: 'La vie familiale et sociale des Indiens Nambikwara' in the *Journal de la Société des Américanistes*, 1948, pp. 1–132.

For instance, groundnuts had an exaggerated increase in area in Senegal when Wolof peasants were spurred on by the money incentive and felt undeterred by the fear of fatigue, since groundnut cultivation requires very little work there. But the cultivation was primitive, and no precautions were taken against the exhaustion or erosion of the soil, and no manure was applied. Hence, in northern Senegal near Luga the soil has already been ruined, and in Cayor in central Senegal it is going the same way.[1] The evil effects of this groundnut cultivation go beyond the borders of the Senegal, for the nuts are partly cultivated by seasonal Navetan workers who come from the Sudan to earn a little ready money, and their labour is lost to the Sudan during the rainy season. The great expansion of the crop is perhaps creating false wealth, because it compromises the future of agriculture in the Senegal and upsets the balance of the economic system in the Sudan.

Soil debasement is also caused by European plantations set up without regard to the peculiarities of tropical pedology. Brazil has been shown to be a case in point, and the West Indies afford a similar illustration. The Europeans found the islands clad in a continuous mantle of forest, for the Caribs used to leave some of the trees standing in their clearings, so that after the patches were abandoned the forest was quickly re-established. On the other hand, the Europeans cleared the ground completely for their tobacco and sugar-cane plantations. Hence, slopes have been laid bare by fierce erosion and large areas are now useless. In Trinidad forest has not reoccupied the area lost as a result of clearing; palm-thickets grow upon the fallow land; then the annual burning destroys the palms and puts in their place a savana-park whose soil is worthless. Réunion and the Cape Verde Islands,[2] which the Europeans found absolutely untouched, have been laid waste in the same way.

[1] The process of soil deterioration may be disguised, checked, or aggravated by rainfall cycles. In a series of rainy years the soil is less affected by æolian erosion and the damage is not so great. If on the other hand a series of rainy seasons are deficient, the Cayor district assumes a semi-desert appearance and the soil becomes a prey to the wind, since it is bare of vegetation. However, as a recent publication shrewdly points out, the abandonment of the Luga area in the Jambur and Cayor districts should perhaps not be regarded as the decisive factor in the deterioration of the soil. The yield of groundnuts was in fact no greater formerly than today, and the harvest was often nil for want of rain, as is the case nowadays. But the Dakar–St. Louis railway—the first constructed in the Senegal—allowed economic crops to be developed in this region first. When another railway was built from Dakar towards the west and opened up rainier and more fertile districts, the weaknesses of Luga showed up clearly, and population and production moved elsewhere. (J. Suret-Canale: 'Quelques aspects de la géographie agraire au Sénégal' in *Les Cahiers d'Outre-Mer*, Bordeaux, 1948, pp. 348–67.)

[2] A. Kopp: 'La vanille dans l'isolement de la canne à sucre à La Réunion' in *Revue de Botanique appliquée et d'Agriculture tropicale*, 1932, pp. 33–47. A. Chevalier: 'Les Iles de Cap Vert,' *id.*, 1935, pp. 734–1090.

The thoughtless introduction of European methods may jeopardize the balance established between natural possibilities and human exploitation. For instance, the introduction of the plough seems to have brought little advantage to Northern Rhodesia.[1] The natives used the *chitimene* system in clearing areas strictly necessary for their food supply.[2] As the population was not numerous, the soil was not overworked. The Europeans brought in the plough and at the same time made it possible for the natives to sell maize and buy a thousand attractive articles with the cash so derived. In districts affected by this development the fields are larger than formerly. The rotation of crops has therefore been shortened; the fields are ploughed into furrows and sown with maize in lines; the crops are no longer mixed; and no manure is used. Thus, all the conditions required for the rapid debasement of the soil by means of erosion and impoverishment are realized. The growth of towns around the administrative centres spurs on production and consequently increases the damage.

The same kind of process has been observed in Southern Rhodesia,[3] where the number of ploughs rose from 3,400 in 1902 to 94,000 in 1938. It was estimated in 1937 that something like one and a half million acres were seriously eroded and that 16 per cent. of the territory had been lost. The introduction of the plough into East Africa is considered dangerous because it favours erosion of the soil.[4] Whilst in 1923 there were 282 ploughs in the Teso country in Uganda, in 1937 there were 15,388. But the advantage of this acquisition was not obvious. No increase in yield was observed when the land was ploughed, for the natives were satisfied with enlarging their fields with the help of the plough, whilst not improving their methods. Besides, as the land is cleared far better by the plough than by the hoe, the natural vegetation is more completely destroyed and is slower in resuming possession of the soil during the period of fallow. It is reported in French West Africa that the introduction of the plough, which is officially encouraged, is causing some uneasiness.[5] No stress is laid here on soil erosion (though there is no reason for supposing that there is no threat of it), but on the danger of turning up the soil too deeply with the plough and of bringing worthless matter to the surface and on the mortal strain imposed on oxen which are out of condition for labour and underfed. Experts do not all agree on

[1] Trapnell and Clothier in 'Ecological Survey of Northern Rhodesia' in the *Scottish Geog. Mag.*, 1938, p. 287.
[2] See above, p. 26.
[3] *Report of the Commission to enquire into the Preservation of the Natural Resources of the Colony*, Salisbury.
[4] Sir Frank Stockdale: *Report on his Visit to East Africa, January–March 1937*, H.M.S.O., London, 1937.
[5] H. Labouret: *Paysans d'Afrique occidentale*, 1941, p. 239.

considering the spread of the use of the plough in Northern Nigeria as an undisputed advantage.

The settlement of Europeans in tropical lands, the social life introduced by them, and the needs of their administration inevitably brought about the rise of the porterage system; and this has become a disastrous burden on the African people, whose traditional economic life has often been upset without any compensating advantage. It must be remembered that it was long the practice to start for the French Chad territory from Brazzaville and to travel by riverboat up the Congo, the Ubanghi, and a right-bank feeder of the latter as far as Fort Sibut; then overland with porters for 150 miles as far as Fort Crampel, whence at high water the journey would be continued by boat on the Gribinghi, a headwater feeder of the Shari. The sparse population of the district between Fort Sibut and Fort Crampel could not cope with the task of porterage. Actually, though the journey was not very long and there was little merchandise to be taken to Lake Chad (300 tons a year), the carriage of this small amount divided into 9,000 loads of between 60 and 65 lb. required 100,000 days' porterage on the Chad–Congo road. The excessive character of this work would have been realized, had there been better knowledge of the hygienic state of the population and its irregular and purely vegetarian diet. However, worn out by the effort demanded of it, the population fled, and the district was deserted. The recruitment of porters became a difficult task which resolved itself into the chief anxiety of the officials. The practical results were lamentable. The carriage of goods from Bordeaux to Fort Lamy, the chief town in the Chad territory, sometimes took eighteen months, was very expensive, and was accompanied by losses that might run to 90 per cent. The parallel development of the road and motor vehicle has enabled an end to be put to this disastrous and at one time unavoidable practice.

About 1924 a considerable part of the labour in Tanganyika Territory was expended in porterage. In the district of Kilosa 400,000 days' porterage was required to meet Government needs alone; and the demands of private trade were far greater. It is recorded that between 6,000 and 7,000 tons of goods were carried to the railway station at Tabora on the heads of negro porters. Each bore about 90 lb. at a time for a distance of some 90 miles, taking at least three days over it. Cotton too required fourteen days' carriage. Thus, the opportunities offered by European trade involved the waste of man-power which would have been better used in producing food. However, the spread of the motor vehicle has abolished porterage in Tanganyika as it has done in the rest of Africa.

Europeans have too often unintentionally carried disorder into tropical countries owing to their great enterprises. Places where railways are being built have become intense centres of malaria, and the story of the Panama Canal is still fresh in our memory. The increased number of road and railway embankments in West Bengal seems to have helped to upset the drainage system and so strengthen the attacks of malaria.[1]

But the question has another side. The construction of railways in tropical regions, that is in regions which are generally sparsely populated, raises an acute problem of man-power. Labour, too often forced, has to be recruited at a distance, and thus the balance of native communities is upset. For reasons given above, the communities make no great use of their agricultural resources and have no reserves. If agriculture is deprived of labour, there is a risk that the crops may decrease and shortage of food caused even in districts some distance from the work. To a great extent this has been the history of the railway from Pointe Noire to Brazzaville. In such conditions the economic balance-sheet of the operation is doubtful.

These unfortunate, though unintentional, consequences of European influence are due to the peculiar conditions of the tropical environment, and the same kind of influence would not have had similar results in temperate surroundings. Some of the harm done, though unintentional also, does not arise, however, from the peculiarities of the tropical environment, but is connected with social and economic changes which have occurred in other physical surroundings too. These changes are due to the brutal clash of cultures at different levels of development.

The Ngonis of Nyasaland[2] had a strong aristocratic and military organization. Their advanced system of agriculture in which erosion was checked by the construction of banks of earth along the contours, included the practice of carefully removing and burying the weeds and was associated with strict discipline. No member of the tribe could shirk his duties in the fields or fail to carry out the instructions given by the chiefs about agriculture. But the hardship of the toil was softened by the pleasure of working together to the rhythm of songs and musical instruments. Social distinctions were great, and only the nobles could be wealthy, wealth and social status being one and the same. Wealth consisted merely of an accumulation of herds of oxen. Differences in standard of living were not marked by the diet, but by the possession of goods which formed the outward signs of wealth. Owing to this social and economic system a population with a density

[1] See above, p. 107.
[2] Margaret Read: 'Native Standards of Living' in Supplement to *Africa*, 1938.

of 100 to the square mile dwelt (and still dwells) in the districts of Dedza and Ncheu. Since the establishment of British rule, the aristocratic and military organization has disappeared; and agriculture has declined owing to the suppression of the social framework which used to encourage the work in the fields. The memory of the former aristocracy persists, but the noble families no longer have a monopoly of the wealth, and different levels of diet are now to be seen, whilst formerly the 'wealthy' ate the same food as the poor. Work in the mines[1] disorganizes agriculture by attracting away many of the men needed in the fields. In the end the women undertake all the agricultural work, but they work carelessly and without any other thought than that of earning money to buy clothes. It is said too that in Uganda the banana plantations, whose upkeep is the women's duty, are less well cultivated than formerly. The large incomes from cotton allow of more frequent travel and enable imported food to be eaten. In fine, the Ngoni of Nyasaland have probably acquired little advantage from contact with European civilization.

A comparison of the density of population in the Amazon valley with that in the central part of the Congo basin is perhaps suggestive. If we compare only what is comparable, that is, the vast equatorial forest,[2] we get a density of 1 in the Amazon valley and 7·5 in the Congo Basin. To explain so great a difference, can we fail to point to the disparity in accessibility in the two regions? The Congo is obstructed in its lower course by impassable rapids; the Amazon is a magnificent waterway, and the *Rio Mar* and its feeders are more easily navigated than the sea. Hence, Europeans have been able to sail up it and inflict the most terrible damage on the natives along the banks by spreading diseases, by slave hunts, and by reducing the people to serfdom. All the evidence points to a sharp fall in the Indian population. Whilst the Portuguese reached the mouth of the Congo in 1482, they did not penetrate into the continent. On the other hand, though they did not found Belem do Pará until 1616, they then quickly explored the Amazon basin.

Since becoming American territory Puerto Rico, which in 1940 had a population of 1,870,000 three-fourths of whom were Europeans and the rest negroes, has been within the customs barriers of the United States. Thus, Puerto Rican sugar was assured of strong protection. The Fordney-McCumber tariff of 1922 placed a duty of 2·2 cents per lb. (about 3*d*. a lb.) on sugar imported into the United States, and Cuban sugar was still paying 2¾*d*. a lb.

[1] See below, p. 129, for fuller details on this point.
[2] In Brazil 1,350,000 sq. m. and in Belgian Congo 366,000 sq. m.

This was an enormous protective tariff, equal at least to the cost price of sugar in Cuba. Under shelter of this barrier Puerto Rican sugar producers were able to make immense profits, since they were protected from the competition of Cuba (as well as Java and other tropical lands) and since their prime costs were lower than those of sugar producers in the United States, who kept prices up at a high level.

These favourable circumstances have brought ruin and unemployment to the Puerto Ricans. In fact, American capital has acquired the land from its former users, who sold it gladly, since the purchase price was high. The peasants, who had once lived off their little holdings in which they grew various crops, now disappeared as such and became employees on the sugarcane plantations which spread uniformly over the once varied countryside. But in order to cut down costs, the big sugar companies gradually rationalized their estates and mechanized their agriculture. The former peasants who had become agricultural labourers, were discharged in large numbers and found themselves without either work or land beside prosperous factories whose profits did not benefit the population. A strange alliance between high tariff walls and the most complete *laisser faire* in economic and social matters has led to this result. The evil can, however, be remedied without great difficulty. By forbidding sugarcane companies to hold more than 500 acres, by buying large properties for cutting up into small holdings, and by promoting industrialization, the authorities have already much improved the position.

In hot, wet regions with a large population European influence has resulted in a rapid growth of this population by reducing the death-rate. Social ills have in fact been effectively combated. But this is a questionable benefit so long as the birth-rate is not lowered and the population increases too fast; for then it is difficult in countries like India to raise or even maintain the standard of living. Some people think that the Colonial system retarded the social development of India and in that way prevented native society from reacting by spontaneously lowering the birth-rate.[1] The towns and industry would never have developed as they have done if India had been independent. Now, it is usually in towns that the first fall in the birthrate takes place, and consequently it is in the towns that the beginning of a fall in the birth-rate might be hoped for. This argument, interesting though it may be, seems invalid, for it rests on

[1] F. W. Nottestein: 'Problems of Policy in Relation to Areas of Heavy Population Pressure' in pp. 138–58 of *Demographic Studies of Selected Areas of Rapid Growth*, Milbank Memorial Fund, 1944.

statistical comparisons and ignores facts in India. In reality[1] no decrease in fertility is reported among the various sections of the Hindu population, in which, according to the above-mentioned theory, a tendency to a demographic decrease should be seen, that is, in the towns and among the upper classes. Besides, complete modernization, which the Colonial system was accused of having prevented, might entail unexpected consequences. For instance, the disappearance of the prejudice against the remarriage of widows would increase the fertility by 14 per cent., assuming widows in India to be no more numerous than in the United States and their fertility to be the same as that of other women. Similarly, the population would increase still more quickly if births no longer took place in the sorry conditions which today often prevail at them.

The Colonial system was responsible for the rapid increase in the population of India because European knowledge and skill lessened the death-rate; but it is unprofitable to try to extend its responsibility. If India's social prejudices and religious superstitions do not weaken, the sub-continent will pass from its population of 389 millions in 1940 to one of 750 millions in 2024, unless demographic catastrophes connected with poverty and political disturbances intervene. India would do well to imitate the example set by the legislature of Puerto Rico. Alarmed at the increase in the island's population, which reached a density of 544 persons to the square mile in 1940, this body decided in 1937 that propaganda in favour of birth-control should no longer be subject to punishment by law.

The economic mischief associated with the Colonial system is more appreciable. In the natural run of things and without any ill intention, a goodly share of the wealth produced in a colony may be lost to it. Thus, researches undertaken in connexion with Belgian Congo have shown that in 1930 between 30 and 40 per cent. of the nominal value of the exports from the colony were absorbed in Belgium and did not remain in the colony. In 1928 when a ton of copper from Katanga was sold for 1,080 francs on export, only 640 francs remained in the colony. The rest went to Belgium in the form of profits, dividends, savings, and pensions.

The harm caused by enterprises frankly inspired by greed and the exploitation of one's fellow men is to be added to the effects of the blows unintentionally struck at the equilibrium of tropical lands. Putting aside facts not clearly associated with the geography of tropical countries, there is no doubt that European colonization in those regions has often been one of exploitation. But it has also been of the same character in temperate lands. Thus, the

[1] Kingsley Davis: 'Demographic Fact and Policy in India,' *id.*, pp. 35–57.

Red Indians and Tasmanians have had no reason to congratulate themselves on European enterprise. What must be remembered here is the harm connected with geographical conditions and especially those in hot, wet regions, *viz.* sparseness of population, poor and easily debased soil, agricultural difficulties, and an environment unfavourable to white colonies of settlement.

The great concessions in French Equatorial Africa and Belgian Congo and the collecting industries they have imposed on the sparse population have impoverished and depopulated the territories in which they have operated. This was a bad system and has failed completely, but was largely due to the difficulty experienced in obtaining commodities for export in an equatorial country, and a sparsely populated one at that. The slave trade was due to the fact that as European planters did not find the necessary labour in America, they had recourse to the unusual and criminal procedure of artificially creating the abundant population they needed. Negroes afforded the additional advantage of being foreign to the country and so unable to escape. Negro Africa supplied an enormous contingent of slaves, though this does not mean that the continent had been densely peopled. But its political and economic condition allowed black traders to deliver the 'ebony-wood' to the Europeans.

Pro-slavery still colours some of the ideas prevalent in various hot, wet lands. At the beginning of 1945 the plantations on the Ivory Coast were still making use of labour which was requisitioned by the Government and was ill paid and badly treated.[1] It was partly the outcome of the difficulty experienced by the planters in finding labour in an unhealthy region, where the people were few in number and weak of body, and was not merely a defect in the Colonial system. Forced labour still exists indeed in Guatemala, which is not a colony. The coffee *fincas* on the lowlands of the Pacific slope have always recruited their labourers in the mountains of the interior. To make this process legitimate, some *finca* owners formed huge estates in the mountains, mainly by seizing communal land. As the Indians were reduced to *peonaje* by debt, they were easily forced to work on the *fincas*. Since Guatemala became independent, much has been done to free the Indians, and *peonaje* for debt has been abolished. But the production of coffee is necessary to the economic system of the country and the Government is reduced, against its will, to resort to forced labour to save the *fincas*. Enforcement of the vagabondage laws constrains the Indians to work on the plantations. Absolute liberty would not ensure the necessary labour for the *fincas* at the right time.[2]

---

[1] All traces of this system have since disappeared.
[2] G. and M. MacCutchen MacBride: 'Highland Guatemala and its Maya Communities' in *Geog. Review*, 1942, pp. 252–68.

36. A *shaduf* worked by two persons. In this as in the scoop shown facing page 113 much ingenuity has been displayed to save muscular effort.

37. Planting out young rice shoots on the Tongking delta. This is hard work, but by ensuring good crops it enables a high civilisation to be built up.

38.

A *seringuero* near Gurupá in Brazil. The white ball at his feet is the rubber he has collected. The black ball is the vessel for holding the latex. An open fire is used for coagulating the latex.

39.

The results of bad cultivation. A former coffee estate on the north-east of the State of Sao Paulo. The hillsides were once covered with coffee bushes, but as no care was taken of the soil, it is now exhausted. The coffee bushes have died out, and new ones will not grow. Apart from small patches in the valley bottom the whole area is now covered with grass which serves merely as pasture for cattle.

The case of Kenya is clearer and more serious. In this equatorial country in which altitude causes the climate to be regarded by Europeans as favourable and pleasant, the coffee bush flourishes and produces berries of good quality. Vast areas of moderately fertile land seemed to be empty because a long war between herdsmen and cultivators had forced the latter to abandon soil they had once tilled. It was easy to give land to the Europeans, and the natives were confined to 'reserves.' In order to have a supply of labour—for the English settlers did not mean to till the land with their own hands, but to direct the work of the natives—two methods of compulsion were used. In the first place, the reserves were too small to hold the Kikuyus and other peoples. Furthermore, heavy taxation forced them to get money by working for wages. The action of the geographical conditions of the tropics is obvious: to free land the Europeans had to dispossess the natives, not knowing that with the burnt-patch system the latter needed far greater area than they cultivated each year. To get labourers in a sparsely peopled country calls for compulsion. And all this effort has been exerted for extremely small results. In 1939 the Europeans, who numbered 21,000 (1,600 being landowners) had at their disposal 15,000 square miles, whilst 3,300,000 natives held only 41,700 square miles in the reserves. In these reserves soil erosion is causing alarming damage, since the land is being subjected to too rapid a rotation of crops and to overstocking. In certain parts of the Kikuyu reserve the average family of six has only 16 acres on which to produce its food, timber, and firewood, pasture its goats, sheep, and at times oxen, and to get something to sell.[1]

The same tendencies are seen in the Rhodesias. In Southern Rhodesia, in 1950, 75,910 square miles were owned by 128,000 Europeans, whilst 50,700 square miles were reserved for the 1,726,000 natives. But in fact the dispossession of the natives is less effective than in Kenya.

As the Rhodesian mines are situated in a typically hot, wet, and therefore sparsely populated district, there would be some difficulty in securing labour did not the taxes imposed on the natives force them to earn wages; for native crops are meant solely for subsistence and leave nothing over for sale.[2] It should be added that the natives in Rhodesia have taken a liking to the small wages paid them in specie and enabling them not only to pay their taxes, but also to buy European goods for which they have no use. But the harm done to native society and its economic system by the work in the mines is immense, and it is no exaggeration to say that demographically,

[1] See Salvadori: *La colonisation européenne au Kenya*, Paris, 1938.
[2] For agriculture in Northern Rhodesia, see above, p. 26.

socially, and economically the Rhodesian natives are in a state of decline.[1] Since a large proportion of and sometimes all the grown men in the villages are employed in the mines, agriculture is disorganized. As female labour is inadequate for the task, the clearings are badly prepared, the ashes are not spread in sufficient quantity on the patches, hoeing is poorly done, and the fences meant to prevent ruminants from browsing on the growing eleusine have not been built. Whilst formerly under the *chitimene* system it was enough to cut off tree-branches to burn in a heap on the patch, the trees are now beginning to be cut down to ground level, a procedure which is quicker, but has the drawback of favouring deforestation. Without the men it sometimes happens that clearings for cassava cannot be made. Now, cassava ensures a supply of food for two years after it is first planted. Consequently, any neglect to plant cassava affects the food-supply for two years. The absence of the young men prevents them from learning from their elders, and the knowledge of the district and its agricultural aptitudes is lost, the natives losing the power to recognize good soil and to adapt themselves to the rhythm of the seasons. In the mines the men get into bad habits which make them dislike the traditional village life, family ties are broken, and venereal diseases are spread. Even the women grow tired of living alone in their villages and move into the mining camps, where they lead immoral lives. Such is the outcome of the successful efforts of the Europeans to get a cheap, ample supply of labour in a country which is sparsely peopled, has poor soil, and whose inhabitants practise subsistence cultivation based on the cleared patch that is allowed to rest by returning to forest.

So far, the balance-sheet of European influence seems burdened with a heavy liability. The tropical environment and native communities have suffered from the introduction of ill-adapted techniques, forced labour, porterage, statute labour, slavery, the transfer of workers from one district to another, sudden changes in the biological surroundings, and new and less favourable social conditions. When the facts are tabulated, it may be said that typical hot, wet lands when sparsely peopled are faced with the following dilemma: economic stagnation and protection of the natives or temporary economic development and the decline of the natives.[2]

Luckily, escape from the dilemma is possible, because European influence has also had beneficial effects wherever it has respected the demands of the geographical environment. First of all,

[1] J. M. Davis: *Modern Industry and the African*, London, 1933.
[2] J. Schwetz: 'Contribution à l'étude de la démographie congolaise' in *Congo* March 1923, p. 305, and March 1924, p. 341.

European science now enables an effective struggle to be made against tropical diseases. Malaria can be cured and, better still, can be eliminated from districts it infests.[1] Where the will exists intestinal troubles can be eradicated; sleeping sickness can be overcome in the victim's own home; and the tsetse fly may be exterminated by the systematic removal of the bush lining the river banks and of certain trees and shrubs which form the favourite haunts of the insect.[2]

But improvement in healthiness should keep pace with the work of economic betterment. It is really impossible to make a very sparsely peopled district healthy, because such areas are too poor to afford the necessary cost and because wild nature occupies most of the surface. Since making a place healthy involves taming nature, healthiness cannot be achieved without the presence of a population large enough to ensure the complete utilization of the land. A large population is a cause rather than a consequence of healthiness. To be lasting and effective, the improvement in healthiness should therefore be achieved first in the more densely peopled districts and then gradually spread step by step with further settlement and the better utilization of the soil. Besides, what is the use of looking after people's hygiene if they are dying of hunger? Medical attention will be of no human interest unless it is accompanied by economic improvement. To keep more children and adults alive while they have to continue to get their living from unirrigated food crops grown on patches cleared by fire might even be held to court disaster and to debase the soil by the faster rotation of fallowing imposed by the necessity of feeding a larger population.

European civilization has opened vast markets to the hot, wet lands and has given them the opportunity of using a world-wide commercial organization together with quick, cheap means of transport. Today the hot, wet regions can sell enormous quantities of their produce on the world market. Now, this produce is mainly supplied by trees, that is, by crops well suited to the soil and climate, since, if they are properly looked after, they reproduce the natural conditions of the forest and in that way prevent erosion and the exhaustion of the soil. Furthermore, they ensure good annual yields and are consequently far more profitable economically than food crops grown in forest patches.

The production of essential oil from oranges in Futa Jallon in French Guinea is a good instance of such a development. The orange

<hr>

[1] See below, p. 134.

[2] J. L. Stewart: *Anti-tsetse Eradication*, paper read before the International Conference of West African Experts, Dakar, 1945. Recently discovered insecticides (D.D.T., etc.) may be a great help and may protect animals from tsetse flies. Besides, it has recently been found that by cross-breeding various species of tsetse fly the dangerous species may be eliminated.

trees are planted in orchards around the Futa huts which are placed wide apart in the villages. The trees used to contribute to the village food-supply, but brought in no money until Europeans taught the natives how to extract the oil from the skin of sweet oranges and bought the produce from them. In 1939 French Guinea had become the greatest exporter of essential oil from sweet oranges; additional income had been secured by the people; and yet neither had the soil been destroyed nor native society disorganized.

The cacao-tree has caused an economic revolution on the Gold Coast. This colony has become the world's leading producer of cocoa, thanks to its favourable climate and a population large enough to ensure the treatment of the beans. As the cacao-tree requires a great deal of labour, it is better suited to cultivation on a family basis than on a large plantation. Social equilibrium is not affected, since the tree is an exclusively native crop; and conditions in no way resemble those in Kenya. If the tree is correctly cultivated, it keeps up the fertility of the soil, for it is a tree and likes growing under other trees for shelter. On the whole, the native population is greatly enriched by cacao-growing and can without difficulty buy from abroad the foodstuffs which it does not produce in sufficient quantity. The Ivory Coast, Nigeria, and the Cameroons have followed the lead.

However, all is not quite right on the Gold Coast, and, for reasons largely connected with ignorance of the principles of tropical geography, weak spots appear. Unwise use of the forest gives cause for fear lest it should disappear entirely. In 1938 there were still 13,500 square miles of forest. As it is being destroyed at a rate of 262 square miles a year, we may well believe that at the end of 50 years there will no longer be a single acre of forest on the Gold Coast. Besides, as the cacao cultivators often fail to protect the crop with shade-trees, the cacao gives the soil an inadequate cover which is far from equivalent to that given by the forest and does not furnish the necessary quantity of organic matter. Cases have already been reported in which the soil has become exhausted under cacao-trees. The disease known as 'swollen shoot' is perhaps connected with the exhaustion of the soil. The people have not shown themselves quite fit to benefit from their prosperity. For instance, the village of Akokoaso was up to its ears in debt.[1] The village is in the centre of the Gold Coast right in the middle of the cacao district. It has the advantage of supplying all its own food. The annual income per family was £21 14s. half of which came from the sale of cacao beans.[2]

[1] W. H. Beckett: *Akokoaso: A Survey of a Gold Coast Village*, London School of Economics, Monographs on Social Anthropology, No. 10, 1943, 96 pp.

[2] Only money income is meant, and produce harvested and eaten by the families is not included in the calculation.

But there were heavy debts consisting of village liabilities (£2,000 for the 1,100 villagers) contracted to carry on lawsuits concerning boundaries with neighbouring villages,[1] and of private obligations amounting to an average of £22 per family. As the interest payable yearly averaged £11 10s. per family, incomes were greatly diminished. This situation can only be explained by want of forethought on the part of the villagers, for they spent money and ran up debts throughout the year, whilst the sale of cacao brought in cash for only four or five months.

Like cacao, other commodities produced for the world market have brought a great improvement in the standard of living of the petty native cultivator. They include palm oil on the shores of the Gulf of Guinea, cotton in Uganda, coffee in Urundi, copra in the East Indies and the Pacific, cloves in Zanzibar, cloves and coffee in Madagascar, and jute in Bengal.

Native agriculture in hot, wet lands has the advantage, therefore, of lending itself to producing export crops. But the methods of native cultivators are often very poor and the improvement in technique derived from following European practice is yet another benefit to place to the credit of Western influence.

From their first arrival in the tropics Europeans established plantations, that is, large joint-stock ventures specializing in the production of goods for export. Instead of being satisfied with buying from the natives produce to be sold profitably in Europe, the settlers established these enterprises because the natives either did not grow the required crops or did not know how to prepare the produce for export. Plantation crops like sugarcane, tobacco, coffee, cocoa, and cotton cannot be exported in their raw state and need preparation, the necessity for which is thus the foundation stone of the plantation system. But European plantations have for long been and still are enterprises involving 'robber economy,' ruining the soil and, when they disappear—as disappear they must—leaving behind them an almost permanent desolation. Whilst native methods of shifting agriculture did no harm to the soil, provided the periods of fallow were long enough, European plantations make the land they occupy barren. Quite recently considerable progress in agricultural technique has brought about the important effect of enabling tree-plantations to be maintained without risk to the future of the soil and without being obliged to abandon the plantation after the expiration of a certain time. Man has gained the mastery over tropical soil.

This achievement has been realized especially in Southeast Asia,

---

[1] Each community in the district was in fact trying to extend its boundaries as far as possible so as to increase its chances of owning gold or diamond fields.

where European plantations cover a greater area than in any other region in the world. Nor is this due to chance; but is chiefly connected with the existence of the largest and most industrious population in the hot, wet belt. Plantation labour is minute compared with the total population and so has easily been able to secure recruits. No other part of the world could have supplied the necessary workers so easily.

A stable economic system and food-supply due to rice cultivation has enabled the workers on the plantations to be fed without difficulty. This would have been impossible on the same scale in Africa, which is poorly supplied by its unirrigated food-crops. Southeast Asia had the advantage of its broken coastline and its position on a sea crowded with traffic, affording opportunities for trade, and bringing in men and enterprise. Lastly, the Chinese have played their part in the development of the plantations both as labourers and, after the first European plantations had been successful, as creative *entrepreneurs*. Their contribution is another extratropical influence on the economic system of the hot, wet lands.

Climate has played its part. It must not be forgotten that the East Indies form the largest region of high rainfall in the world. But outside Asia there are many regions with a climate favourable to plantations. Fertile soil of volcanic origin has favoured some plantations, as in the case of the basic soil of the tobacco plantations in the district of Deli in Sumatra. But on the whole soil has not been a determinant. The *hevea* and the tea plant do not demand great fertility.

The plantations have been able to develop without harming traditional activities and without dispossessing the natives, for they have been established in gaps in the population (see Figs. 14 and 15). This is a fortunate result of the distribution of population, which has given almost empty districts in some places and patches of high density in others.[1]

But as the areas thus open to plantations were avoided by man, they were of course unhealthy. Malaria formed the chief obstacle to settlement in them. But methodical investigation has permitted the enemy to be mastered, and, where the will exists, plantation areas are now healthy. This is a priceless contribution to the development of tropical lands. But the elimination of malaria is possible only because the plantations use the whole area and substitute wholly man-controlled surroundings for the natural environment. The elimination of malaria could not be achieved in a district in which burnt-patch cultivation was practised, for, by that system, wild nature continues to occupy the greater part of the area. In Malaya it is estimated that

[1] See above, p. 104.

one worker is needed for every seven acres of *heveas*, which gives a density of 260 persons to the square mile, taking into account the workmen's families and the non-agricultural population (see Figs. 14 and 15).

The destruction of the haunts of the anopheles larvæ is a necessary,

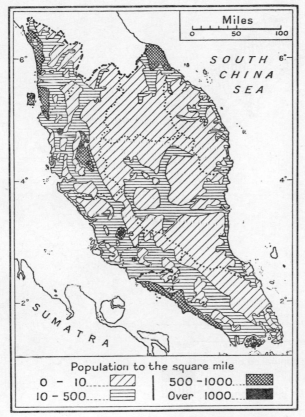

FIG. 14. Density of population in Malaya
(After C. A. Vlieland, 'The Population of the Malay Peninsula,' in *Geog. Review*, 1934)

but sufficient, condition of the elimination of malaria. As the plantations occupy ground that is not flooded, they do not have to struggle against *A. umbrosus* (which seeks out calm, shady water for its larvæ) but against a species of anopheles whose larvæ like clear, clean, flowing water reached by the sun's rays. Nothing pleases them better than the unevenness of the banks of a sun-bathed brook whose water flows along not too fast. These habits occur, for instance, in

Assam in *A. minimus*, *A. fluviatilis*, and *A. culicifacies*. Such peculiarities explain why clearing the forest and draining the marshy bottoms generally starts terrific epidemics of malaria, because these changes in the surroundings make conditions favourable to the most danger-

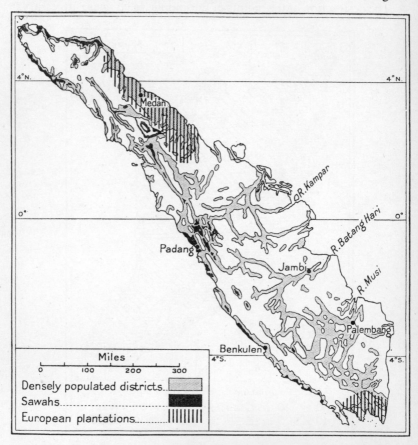

F**ig**. 15.   Sumatra, showing areas cleared of forest and distinguishing inhabited strips and European plantations.

The unshaded portions have not been cleared of forest, for human settlement is discontinuous here as always in an equatorial region.

(After Herbert Lehmann, 'Die Bevölkerung der Insel Sumatra,' in *Petermanns G. Mitteilungen*, 1938)

ous species of anopheles. People used to talk of 'forest fever' and of the damage done by 'miasma' in the forest! An exact knowledge of the complex of the anopheles acquired in Malaya between 1900 and 1910 now makes it possible to overcome malaria. The drainage must be carefully arranged so as to restrict the area attended to. Streams must be given as straight a course as possible and their banks clear-cut and, if possible, cemented in such a way as to remove all the irregularities. They should be shaded by lines of carefully trimmed bushes. This method of intermittent drainage should clean out all the mosquito haunts, and of course as an extra precaution no pools should be allowed near houses. Lastly, certain especially dangerous and critical spots should be coated with oil or sprinkled with Paris green or some other insecticide. Attention should be concentrated on the permanent haunts, for they are really extremely dangerous, since from them come the anopheles which at the beginning of the rainy season lay their eggs in the little pools formed by the rain. It stands to reason that if the permanent haunts are destroyed the little hollows which are filled with water at the very beginning of the rains can no longer become breeding places.

The results are splendid. On some estates in Malaya the mosquitoes have disappeared, and people sleep without mosquito nets. In a country like Assam, which is more broken and more difficult to develop, if the state of things before the attack of malaria began in 1927 is compared with the state in 1938 after its commencement, the progress is as follows:—

	1927	1938
Population	17,770	18,670
Death rate per thousand	31·5	21·4
Days of illness	249,306	147,993
Splenic index in children	60 %	14·3 %

In spite of improvement in precautions against malaria, certain places cannot be made healthy; for instance, the railway station of Krong Pha at the foot of the escarpment of the central hill-mass in southern Annam. As the river is too strong, too rapid, and too irregular to be controlled, it will always be infested with anopheles. The sole, but infinitely too expensive, remedy would be to cover over the river for a distance of nearly two miles.[1]

Thanks to European scientific research, agricultural technique has made great progress in the provinces of soil protection, yield, and the quality of the product. In the protection of the soil—a matter of fundamental importance in the hot, wet regions[2]—plantations start with the advantage derived from their shrub or tree crops of fixing the soil and adding leaves and twigs to its organic elements.[3]

[1] This opinion was expressed to the author at Dalat on April 26, 1946, by Dr. H. G. S. Morin.
[2] See above, p. 19.
[3] This applies only to plantations of trees and shrubs which occupy the ground for ten years or more. With tobacco and sugarcane the case is different. Besides,

But that is not enough, for the example of Brazil shows clearly that tropical soils do not stand up to unskilful coffee cultivation.[1] In the neighbourhood of Singapore the vegetation does not altogether hide the denuded lateritic soil whose dull red colour can be seen on the sites of former rubber plantations that have been abandoned owing to the complete exhaustion of the soil. The history of soil-protecting methods on rubber plantations is of the greatest interest. It shows the progressive discovery of Nature's demands in the tropics and the steps taken to comply with them in order to achieve success. On early rubber plantations crops of cassava, pine-apples, gambier, and bananas were grown between the young trees up to the sixth year. This exhausting practice has been abandoned because it promoted erosion. To keep the soil quite bare under the rubber trees according to the system of 'clean weeding' was also thought necessary, and the soil in old plantations was ruined in that way both in Malaya and Ceylon.[2]

Attention is now wholly concentrated on the struggle against erosion and the exhaustion of the soil. Various processes have been perfected one after another and are now used more or less concurrently. They consist of discontinuous ditches staggered along the contours; of terraces supported by walls or bush-clad slopes; and of covering plants to protect the soil, retain it, and enrich it with humus.[3] As these plants might interfere with the rubber trees, a bare circular patch is sometimes made round the foot of each tree; or else the covering plants are arranged in rows parallel with the lines of *heveas*. The latest plan when laying out a plantation is neither to dig nor to clear away the bush, whose removal is reduced to the minimum needed for planting the rubber trees. The original vegetation is then progressively weeded out, so that only the most suitable species are kept. In this way there is an unbroken transition from the original forest to the full-grown rubber plantation with its undergrowth. The soil is never laid bare and so does not suffer from erosion. A great

these plants usually grow on alluvial soil on the lowlands, that is, on land which can as easily and as profitably be devoted to swamp rice; *cp.* the alternation of sugarcane and rice on the *sawahs* in Java. It is very risky to grow tobacco on the slopes of mountains, for the unprotected soil suffers greatly from erosion. For instance, the first European tobacco plantations in Nyasaland laid waste the soil. For the West Indies and Réunion, see p. 121.

[1] See above, p. 69.

[2] It has been observed in Uganda that clean weeding on plantations of *Markhamia platycalyx* led to the debasement of the soil and the unhealthy condition of the trees. This is partly explained by the fall of drops of water which, coming from the tops of the trees, eroded the bare soil, unprotected as it was, since fallen leaves were quickly destroyed by termites.

[3] These are either creepers (*Centrosema pubescens, Calopogonium mucoides, Dolichos Hosei, Pueraria phaseoloides*, and *Mikamia scandens*) or bushes (*Lamtoro, Tephrosia candida, Crotalaria anagyroides*). The preponderance of Leguminosæ is noticeable.

deal of knowledge has been needed and trouble required in order to
perfect the simplest technique and avoid flying in the face of Nature.

It is now established that the exhaustion of the soil is due, not to
cultivated plants, but to the cultivator's lack of skill, which causes
the destruction of the humus and the removal of nitrogen and bases
from the soil. Hence, if the preservation in the soil of its fertile elements is ensured, the cultivated plant will be adequately nourished,
and the soil will not be exhausted. All researches point in the same
direction. It has been noticed that oil-palm plantations are less
destructive of the soil than any other[1] although this palm (*elæis*)
requires a great deal of mineral food—312 lb. of mineral substances
per acre per annum against 107 for coffee and 53 for the *hevea*. But
the preliminary clearing for a plantation of oil palms is moderate and
does not go as far as the removal of tree-stumps, and, furthermore,
a thick cover of leguminous plants is ensured. Lastly, the *elæis* yields
far more ligno-cellulose matter than either the *hevea* or the coffee
bush. On the other hand, the fact that the coffee bush will not
flourish in sandy soil is not due to the soil being really too poor for it.
The truth is that ruthless clearing, the bare state of the soil for months,
and the use of covering plants which give little protection or improvement ruin the soil in a short time.[2] It is now known that tree plantations can be made without danger to the soil if all steps are taken to
render conditions as nearly like those of the forest as possible by
securing protection from erosion, reducing percolation, maintaining
a temperature of not more than 77° or 78° F., and supplying plenty
of woody organic matter. It is known furthermore that, if the
requirements of cultivated plants are complied with, tree plantations
are more or less easily managed in a way most favourable to soil
conservation. The *elæis* is the most accommodating of these crops,
and the *hevea*, the cacao-tree, and the coffee bush follow in progressive order of harmfulness to the soil. Of course, annual unirrigated
crops grown without forest cover and on weeded ground cause the
maximum degree of damage.

An innovation of European science has been to make up by an
application of chemical manure for the good taken from the soil—at
least, when the soil will allow it, for tropical soils do not all respond
to chemical manure. Manure used to form a considerable proportion
of the weight of merchandise carried from north to south through
the Suez Canal.

So then, by trial and error the European planter has found a way
of escape from the dangers which used to threaten tree plantations
owing to the ease with which the soil could be ruined. This is

---

[1] See A. Beirnaert, *op. cit.*, *supra*, p. 79.
[2] *Id.*, *ibid.*, p. 78.

certainly one of the greatest contributions of European science to tropical agriculture.[1]

Scientific research has, moreover, enabled yields to be increased. By means of plant selection, the control of fertilization, and grafting, rubber plantations have raised their yield of crêpe per acre from 3·2 cwt. to 9·5 cwt. Other plantation crops have made similar progress. The oil-palm, though a native of Guinea, gives far higher yields in Sumatra than in Africa.

By copying improved methods and borrowing plant selections from European plantations the natives can better their own crops. By a natural development native planters become rivals of the Europeans who set them on the path of progress. And they are dangerous rivals, since the petty native growers do not have to worry about cost price or interest on capital. Indonesia has already shown what such a development could be at the start. Henceforth the advantage of European plantations does not lie so much in the yield as in a better presentation of the tea, coffee, rubber, palm oil, sugar, or sisal owing to its treatment in large quantities in modern factories. But native growers might overcome this handicap by means of co-operative factories. Whatever the future may bring, however, the part played by European plantations has been enormous. They have proved the possibility of obtaining high, steady yields from tree plantations in areas of broken relief in hot, wet regions while maintaining the soil and its fertility. They have equally proved the possibility of eliminating malaria. Perhaps their influence will cause a demographic and economic revolution in tropical lands.[2]

---

[1] A particularly striking example of wisdom in treating soil is given by a plantation at Sukamendi in Java, on which sisal is grown in rotation with cassava. The rotation consists of one crop of sisal and two of cassava. So the plantation has a tapioca mill and a sisal mill. Sisal and cassava have been chosen because they do not have the same requirements. The former needs a fertilizing mixture in which phosphate of potash predominates, the latter a mixture with nitrogen predominating. The second crop of cassava is moreover heavily manured. The water used in both mills is spread over the whole area of the plantation by gutters. In that way nearly everything taken from the soil by the crop is restored (G. Oudot in *Bulletin économique de l'Indochine*, 1940, pp. 76–91.) The sisal mill on the plantation at Taveta in Kenya used the same method of returning the good to the soil.

[2] The attempt by the British Government to produce groundnuts in East Africa on a large scale by means of vast capital expenditure on mechanical processes is now an admitted failure. Whilst the plan formed in 1947 envisaged the planting of 1,200,000 acres with groundnuts by 1949, in fact only 23,000 acres were so planted.

CHAPTER 12

CONCLUSION

THE tropics are inferior to the temperate regions in a number of ways. Although it is still impossible to assert that hot, wet climates are naturally less favourable to physical and mental activity, it is only too certain that these climates permit the development of a large number of infectious diseases which make the tropical environment less favourable to mankind than temperate latitudes are. Great heat and a heavy rainfall are disastrous to the quality and stability of arable soil, and a plot of ground temporarily cultivated and abandoned as soon as the plot shows signs of exhaustion—and it soon shows them—is the tropical cultivator's answer to such conditions of soil. Insect-carried diseases and the poverty of the soil do not encourage stock-rearing; the economic value of equatorial forests is not equal to their luxuriance; and the coal resources of hot countries are poor. Tropical lands suffer from the drawbacks of being divided into three sections completely separated by broad oceans. Between them, and even between tropical Asia and equatorial Africa, cultural relations have been very difficult and consequently very slight. Agricultural methods are not easily communicated except within the climate in which they originate, nor do they spread, except along parallels of latitude. Hence, isolated from one another by the outline of the continents, the tropical lands in each land-mass have developed independently. These conditions were not very favourable to the progress of civilization. On the other hand, the temperate lands of Europe, Asia, and Africa as a whole offered by their cohesion far greater possibilities of cultural exchange and mutual fertilization of ideas.

It is not surprising that tropical lands should as a whole be thinly populated and that they should be backward in civilization. The contribution of these regions to the fund of world civilization is small, whether in the material, intellectual, or moral sphere. How could the population be dense, how could it build up a high civilization, when it was enfeebled by many serious diseases, when the agricultural system, though proper to the climate, yields a precarious existence, and when the soil has not been mastered?

And yet it is not impossible to control elusive tropical nature and to build up teeming and highly civilized communities in hot, wet lands. The case of tropical Asia is very significant in this respect. India, Indo-China, and Java were and are the homes of swarming

141

populations and advanced civilizations. The economic foundation of the mighty structure is the cultivation of swamp rice and irrigation. The cultivation of swamp rice is the only means capable of ensuring a steady, abundant supply of cereals in tropical lands. The fact is, the flooded ricefield does not exhaust the soil or expose it to erosion, and it can yield adequate crops once and even twice a year for hundreds and thousands of years. It is therefore a suitable basis for an increasingly large and highly civilized population whose stability is ensured by its mastery of the soil. Whilst the unirrigated cultivation of food crops year by year is a precarious, unstable business and cannot result in feeding large populations, the cultivation of swamp rice enables man to escape from the worry of getting a pittance day by day and even from suffering famine, and so allows him to develop the higher aspects of civilization. Besides, the densely populated regions of tropical Asia are less unhealthy than the average hot, wet country. This advantage is due to the utilization of the whole area and the complete domestication of nature.

But the exceptional development of tropical Asia is indubitably linked with cultural influences brought from outside the tropics. A comparison between Africa south of the Sahara and India is very instructive (see Fig. 16). Except in the Union, Southern Rhodesia, and Kenya, and, in more recent times, parts of West Africa, the former has remained in a backward condition. Cultural influences from the Mediterranean and the East are not wanting, but have had little effect since the Sahara has checked their spread in two ways. First of all, because it is a difficult obstacle, a door not easily forced. Secondly, because it forms a broad climatic and biological gap in which life is not now possible in a belt twenty degrees of latitude wide. Consequently, the methods of utilizing nature and the cultural influence of the Eastern Mediterranean and Southwestern Asia have not been able to pass by successive steps from the temperate Mediterranean environment to the hot, wet belt, and there have been no transitional zones to permit progressive adaptation. Cultural influence and methods of using nature's gifts cannot easily jump over twenty degrees of latitude. The geographical conditions by which the worst hot desert in the world stretches uninterruptedly from the Atlantic to the Persian Gulf are therefore largely responsible for the backward character of civilization in Africa south of the Sahara. The wet periods in the Quaternary era ended too soon to permit cultural exchanges.

On the other hand, southern India with its dark-skinned population is linked uninterruptedly with the north, and expanses of steppe interspersed with well-watered valleys join northern India to eastern and northern Persia, Russian Turkistan, Bactria, and, consequently, with

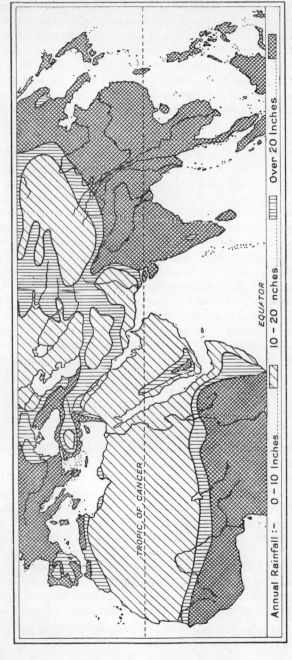

FIG. 16. Rainfall in the Old World, showing that Africa south of the Sahara is isolated, whilst India and Southeast Asia are connected with the temperate belt by zones of high rainfall.

Susiana, Mesopotamia, Syria, and Asia Minor. Gradual adaptation by stages has been possible from Bactria or Chaldæa on the one hand to Cape Comorin on the other, first in Gandhara, then in Sind, then in the Punjab, Bengal, and many other places. Similarly, in eastern Asia the climate places no obstacle and causes no gap between Siberia and Java. By allowing cultural influence and methods of making use of nature's gifts to pass from the temperate belt by progressive adaptation to the tropical region, the climatic factors have favoured the rise of a very different kind of human geography in hot, wet Asia from that in Africa south of the Sahara.

A significant instance of the effect of cultural influence on human geography is afforded by recent observations on the Pacific coast of Colombia. The coast and more favourable districts have been deserted by the Chocó Indians, who have withdrawn to remote areas and thus given way to the negroes. The latter seem more active and enterprising and to be endowed with greater vitality. They tend to form more considerable social and political groups than do the Chocós. In short, they seem better adapted to the tropical environment. But such a conclusion would be hasty, for it would rest neither on adequate data nor on a knowledge of the reactions of the Chocó Indians to the tropical climate as compared with those of the African negroes. It is wiser to remember that the negroes are the descendants of 'maroons,' or slaves who had run away from plantations in the north. Besides being as well adapted as the Indians to the tropical environment, the negroes have been to some degree initiated into a higher civilization and better methods. In a modest, but indubitable manner they are, as compared with the Chocó Indians, the representatives of European civilization. In the circumstances it is not surprising that they should get the better of the Indians, since these have remained in a more primitive state.[1]

The cultivation of swamp rice and to a lesser degree the use of irrigation in other tropical regions produce the same results as they do in southern Asia. There is no physical reason why areas of recent alluvium in the valleys and lowlands of Africa and America should not be developed in the same way as their counterparts in Asia. The facilities which modern civilization has made available for the spread of technical knowledge would render these changes possible.

But modern civilization opens many other prospects for tropical lands. Thanks to chemical and biological discoveries achieved in the temperate belt, it places at their disposal remedies and technical methods which enable them to struggle against endemic diseases

[1] R. C. Murphy: 'The Littoral of Pacific Colombia and Ecuador' in *Geog. Review*, 1939, pp. 1–33.

in the tropics. Man can now be cured and countries made healthy, so long as the work of improving the conditions of health is accompanied by complete utilization of the land, for the conquest of disease must keep pace with the control of nature.

Improvement in healthiness must go hand in hand with the utilization of the land. Neither can exist without the other. The healthiness of a wild country or of a territory with few persons to the square mile cannot be improved. That is why one of the most effective ways of developing backward tropical countries would be to concentrate the population in a portion of the area to be developed. No attention should be paid to expanses which have been completely abandoned, but intensive efforts should be focussed on the part now adequately peopled.[1] This would afterwards be the starting-point for the scientific colonization of the territory which had been temporarily abandoned. Something rather like this was done at Anchau in Nigeria, where, after finding that the scattered population could not be cured of sleeping sickness, the authorities concentrated the people in part of the district.[2]

Modern civilization opens up the world market to the products of tropical plantations. Their coffee, tea, cocoa, and rubber can be sold to the rest of the world in exchange for the food they do not grow well, that is, unirrigated cereals like wheat, and for the produce of the livestock farmer. Better still, modern science, in the development of which the tropical regions have had no share, has perfected the technical devices that preserve the soil on the plantations, ensure the production of crops for an unlimited time, and increase the yields. As in the case of the communities in tropical Asia, the advance of tropical peoples towards a higher civilization and a large population will be brought about by cultural elements evolved in regions outside the hot belt.

Thus, in a self-balancing world-economic-system, that is, in a perfectly free or in a voluntarily regulated system, in what a wag used to call 'world-wide autarchy,' the place of tropical lands is clearly marked. They should provide 'colonial goods,' or, more accurately, commodities supplied without danger to the soil by scientifically conducted plantations of trees. So they will play an essential part in the world's economic system and will have a place which no other climatic belt can take from them. In the circumstances they will be able to enhance their wealth, establish healthy conditions, and increase their population. But this demographic increase should not

[1] See Pierre Gourou: *Problèmes du monde tropical, Les cahiers d'Outre-Mer* (Bordeaux), 1948, pp. 9–13.
[2] See T. A. M. Nash: *The Anchau Rural Development and Settlement Scheme*, H.M.S.O., 1948.

lead to an expansion of the area cultivated annually with unirrigated food-crops. Such an expansion could be obtained only by accelerating the rhythm of the crops, that is, by a reduction in the period of fallow, and, lastly, by wasting the fertility of the soil and causing its deterioration. A more numerous population should be fed by a more and more intensive cultivation of swamp rice or by importing food from the temperate lands.

The new economic tendencies which are appearing and the plans put forward to ensure a better economic system in tropical countries, as in the rest of the world, must be judged by taking into account the peculiar characteristics of the human and economic geography of the tropics.

No one disputes the need to raise the standard of living in all countries and especially in those that are poorest. It is said that all countries are interdependent, that poverty in some causes poverty in others, and that there cannot be a wealthy country if there are wretched ones. 'Poverty anywhere constitutes a danger for prosperity everywhere' was the cry at the Conference of the International Labour Office at Philadelphia in 1944. An expanding economic system, which by continuous progress will do away with economic crises and ensure the prosperity of the world, requires that poor countries should no longer exist and in fact calls for universal increase in consumption.

Let us see what this means so far as tropical lands are concerned. To raise the standard of living of tropical peoples the first step is to abolish the *ladang* system of shifting cultivation on patches cleared by burning, since it is incompatible with a high standard of living. Then again, terraced ricefields must be abolished, since the tiny terraces demand human toil out of all proportion to the result obtained. Thirdly, the density of the rural population in the overcrowded regions of tropical Asia must be considerably reduced, because the existing excessive number of cultivators will be able to reach a higher standard of living only if in reduced numbers they till larger fields and use more effective methods. So work will have to be found for the crowds that are unemployed through the disappearance of the *ladangs* and numerous terraced ricefields and the relief from congestion of the overcrowded lowlands. Can these swarms of human beings be employed in industry or in new agricultural work, such as the cultivation of swamp rice in lowlands still unused and the creation of tree plantations? The significance of so far-reaching a revolution in the social and economic spheres should be fully realized.

Raising the standard of living will also stir up serious problems for the tropical plantations. Tropical lands seem indeed to have a solid advantage over temperate regions in the production of cane-sugar, oleaginous matter, various kinds of latex and gum, and specifically tropical products, like coffee and vanilla; but certain factors in the superiority of the tropics may weaken in the future. Among these the very low price of labour is not the least. If the standard of living and, consequently, wages go up, the prime costs of commodities will become heavier. Tropical oil-yielding crops will perhaps no longer dominate the market from the day when the agricultural labourer who produces groundnuts in Senegambia or copra in Celebes has needs as great as those of an English or American farmhand. The large-scale production of oil from soya beans in the United States is already a threat to the prosperity of tropical countries which produce oleaginous commodities. The United States, which were formerly large-scale importers of oil, are now exporters. What would happen if tropical countries saw their expenses increased by a rise in the standard of living?

Tropical produce has the advantage, too, of being derived from new countries. The plantations were formed a short while ago, usually on a concession, and do not find their prime costs burdened by the dead weight imposed in old countries by the price of land. This advantage will gradually end with time, as sales and changes of ownership give the land a price.

The plantations benefit from another advantage. As they have recently been set up and operate on a large scale, they often have a technical superiority over agriculture in the temperate belt. The technical improvements on the tobacco plantations at Deli or on certain rubber plantations in Cochin China have few equals in temperate lands. But this feature is linked with large holdings and will disappear with them. If small-scale native holdings replace large-scale European plantations, the yields, the quality of the produce, and the prime costs will all be greatly affected. Yet it is probable that political and social needs will encourage this change in the system of land utilization, which will in the end lessen the economic advantage possessed by tropical countries. The advantage will diminish all the more because agriculture in the temperate belt will on its side make appreciable technical progress through the development of co-operative institutions and research departments. It is not absurd to imagine such technical progress in agriculture in the temperate regions as will make the sale of tropical rice and maize impossible in our latitudes.

A rise in the standard of living of tropical peoples will therefore raise very great problems; perhaps far more than it will solve. Must not the root of all these difficulties be ultimately found in the poverty of tropical soils, which do not allow those who cultivate them to reach the same standard of living as farmers in the temperate belt?

Industrialization, in which some people see the remedy for all our economic ills, would enable work to be given to the crowds who are unemployed owing to the disappearance of occupations which a rise in the standard of living has made impracticable. Here again we must try to see clearly so as not to be led away by illusions which, whilst mistaken, are not even generous. Industry must certainly be developed in tropical lands; industrial methods perfected in temperate lands— and not in tropical countries—ought certainly to be introduced into the hot, wet belt. Industrial development must be encouraged when natural conditions are favourable, and especially when to the natural resources are added enormous supplies of labour, as is the case in southern Asia. The Tongking delta, which has large quantities of coal—though not of coking coal—a plentiful supply of lime, and a large population, has special advantages for the establishment of certain heavy industries. There is no better place for the production of cement, and in a well organized world the cement factories of the country should be able to export their produce far and wide. It is no less evident that India's resources in coal and hydro-electricity should be used to the full.

It would perhaps be dangerous to go beyond the possibilities of coal and water-power, but the overcrowded countries in southern Asia should use their plentiful and hardworking man-power in crafts which produce articles intended for local consumption and even for export and which do not risk the competition of mass-produced goods. Such crafts when modernized and using electric current and improved tools would have their roots in ancient tradition. In Annam, Assam, Borneo, and Guatemala villages specialize in particular manufactures. A substantial addition of wealth would thus be ensured to the teeming population in southern Asia and the rise of enormous urban proletariats would be avoided.

But the industrialization on principle of all tropical countries, even those that are thinly peopled, would raise very serious difficulties if carried far and developed systematically. Economists, chiefly American, have formed on this subject views which, though interesting, do not escape criticism. They emphasize the fact that American trade is particularly active with highly industrialized countries like Great Britain and Canada, whilst it is small with countries whose economic system is backward. But it would be a very different matter for a country which tried to develop a large industrial system based on heavy industries in a world in which such industries are already plentiful and, thanks to their natural advantages and technical methods, produce at a cost that industries newly formed in tropical

countries could not hope to equal. In these circumstances the formation of new industries would be impossible without tariff protection.
India is already protecting her industries, and the Bombay Plan looks
forward to an autarchic development of Indian industry under shelter
of various customs duties. Brazilian heavy metallurgy at Volta
Redonda in the Rio Doce district is maintained by a tariff. To think
that the industrialization of tropical countries will lead to an increase in trade is a pious hope. But it may just as easily end in
national autarchy. The experience of recent years leads one rather to
believe that the tendency to autarchy will win the day, for it rests on
anxiety to defend the country, on an ill-understood ideal of national
independence, and on the narrow interests of local capitalists or
workers. Now, owing to the special conditions of agriculture in the
tropics, self-sufficiency is fraught with danger to the region.

In fact, if the hot, wet lands are forced by the rise of autarchy to
rely exclusively on their own resources to feed their growing populations, if they cannot buy food abroad in exchange for the produce of
their own plantations, they will have to turn for supplies, first, to a
frantic increase in swamp rice cultivation; then, when the possibilities of this are exhausted, to the raising of annual food-crops without
irrigation. But this is incompatible with a high standard of living.
It lends itself to a system of domestic economy, but does not lead to
trade; and, if cultivation is unwisely expanded in response to the
urgent needs of the population, it ruins the soil and compromises
the future. The history of the Mayas should not be forgotten.

Autarchy may come from two directions, both equally harmful to
tropical countries. In the first place, the countries in the temperate
belt may develop autarchic tendencies and so reduce their purchases
in tropical lands. The latter will then be forced to fall back on their
own resources and will be caught in the disastrous toils leading to
the ruin of the cultivable soil. Certainly, there are commodities in
which tropical countries hold an unbreakable monopoly, viz. coffee,
tea, and cocoa—always assuming that their use is not artificially
reduced in temperate lands. But many other tropical products run
the risk of being eliminated by autarchy. The intertropical belt certainly has a real advantage over the temperate zone in sugar production, for canesugar is produced at a lower cost than beetsugar; and
in a well-thought-out world-economic-system sugar ought to come
from the tropics, provided that all precautions have been taken to
prevent soil erosion on sugarcane plantations. Yet the sale of tropical
canesugar is hampered by tariffs which temperate countries have
set up to protect their beetsugar cultivation. For instance, the
United States, which are so keen on the industrialization of tropical

lands, used practically to shut out sugar from Java, though it came from an overcrowded tropical country; whilst they encouraged settlement in Hawaii and protected their own sugar planters, who, however, produced at a far higher price. Would it not be simpler and of greater service to mankind to let sugar from Java enter the United States, which in exchange would sell manufactured goods to Java, than to try to create in Java a modern industry which would need protection against American competition?

What is true of sugar is equally true of tobacco and may become true of rubber, if American *guayule* and, more particularly, *kok-saghiz* on the steppes of Asia are improved in yield and become objects of autarchic protection. The sale of tropical vegetable oil may similarly be threatened by the progress of soya oil production.

Tropical plantations are seriously jeopardized by synthetic goods, whose manufacture arose from a desire for self-sufficiency and is being encouraged for the same reason. Synthetic rubber, synthetic *chicle* (the basis of chewing gum), vanillin, various plastics, chemical dyes, modern methods of treating fatty substances, synthetic quinine and other synthetic anti-malarial drugs, synthetic varnish, and rayon and other artificial fibres are all dangerous rivals to tropical agriculture. At present costs synthetic products do not cut out the cultivated articles, but they set a maximum price for tropical produce. The misfortune which threatens tropical agriculture will not affect temperate agriculture to the same extent. Is this fact a further proof of that inferiority of tropical to temperate lands, of which examples have been given above? It would be a mistake to think so; for temperate lands would in fact suffer less from the progress of chemistry because they have already eliminated from their agricultural production those commodities which would be exposed to suffer from that progress. This elimination occurred in the early days of chemistry, as in the case of madder dye; but more especially it was due to the competition of tropical products which were marketed in large quantities owing to progress in the means of transport. Thus, textile crops and, at least for a time, oil-yielding plants have disappeared from temperate countries;[1] but temperate agriculture has entrenched itself in impregnable positions in the production of cereals, meat, milk, vegetables, and fruit. Tropical countries are now exposed to the attacks of chemical industries because they replaced temperate lands as suppliers of vegetable oil products and expecially of vegetable raw materials for industry.

Secondly, autarchy may spring from tropical lands themselvesr for they might develop their industries in order to preserve thei,

---

[1] But temperate countries have returned to the vegetable oil market with soya oil from Manchuria and the United States.

national independence or because of their conviction that industrialization, even if autarchic, would be a means of raising the standard of living of the people. If, as is very probable, these industries are protected by tariffs or import quotas, such measures will inevitably cause previous customers to retaliate by reducing their purchases of agricultural goods derived from the tree plantations in the tropical country which began the tariff war.[1]

In short, the chances of autarchy in our times are great. The beauty of liberty is praised everywhere, and the autarchy of the Communist systems is hated. But words and actions hardly ever agree. Economic control inspires the economic measures adopted in the various countries, and economic control is very close to autarchy. Autarchic prospects are not very pleasant for the people in tropical lands, since their standard of living cannot be greatly raised, if the system becomes firmly established.

To sum up, it will not be easy to raise the standard of living of tropical people if Nature's directions are obeyed; but it will be utterly impossible if her vetoes are disregarded. In the last resort, shifting vegetable plots, *rays*, *ladangs*, or *milpas*, are incompatible with a high standard of living and will disappear if tropical peoples reach the standard of the most highly developed countries in Europe or America. Furthermore, such methods of cultivation cannot answer the needs of a growing population. Numerous and prosperous populations in the tropics should look for their food supply to the cultivation of swamp rice on low ground, to irrigation, to the possibilities of trade afforded by the sale of commodities obtained from tree plantations run in such a way as to maintain the fertility of the soil, and to a convenient degree of industrial development. By paying attention to these principles the hot, wet lands will one day be able to enjoy steady prosperity and to play an increasing part in the economic life of the world. They will be able to attain that life which is free from famine, want, and poverty, which begets intellectual and moral progress, and which, in spite of disillusion, is prayed for by those who have not lost hope of seeing the majority of mankind in this world enjoying an abundance of wealth. Geography is not an abstract study. It cherishes a desire or hope to secure

---

[1] It may be claimed that these difficulties can be overcome by having recourse to a 'triangular' trade. For instance, the United States might sell machine tools to China, which might sell cheap cotton goods to Java, which might sell rubber to the United States. In this way the financial circle would be closed. Matters might be arranged theoretically in that way, but the actual practice to which nationalism and demands of labour have accustomed us would rather be as follows:—The Chinese would try to build up a rubber industry in their country by using caoutchouc from Java; the Javanese would try to establish cotton and rubber industries; and the Americans would endeavour to maintain their synthetic rubber industry.

practical results. By rendering a better understanding of the exact nature of man's relation to his surroundings and by pointing out the immense influence of culture, geography suggests that there is nothing fixed and rigid in that relation and that it can be modified in a way that is favourable to man. The physical world does not exert a determinist influence on man, who is master of his destiny if he is conscious of this mastery. It is certain, however, that nothing worth while will be realized if the attention of the modern world is focussed solely on the means of living. What is needed even more is an art of living.

INDEX

153